Flipping
the Script
on
INFERTILITY

Published under licence by Brown Dog Books and
The Self-Publishing Partnership, 7 Green Park Station, Bath BA1 1JB

www.selfpublishingpartnership.co.uk

ISBN printed book: 978-1-83952-204-8
ISBN e-book: 978-1-83952-205-5

Cover design by Kevin Rylands
Internal design by Andrew Easton

Printed and bound in the UK

This book is printed on FSC certified paper

MIX
Paper from
responsible sources
FSC
www.fsc.org
FSC® C013604

Flipping the Script on INFERTILITY

Taking back control of life and purpose

KEZIA ASHLEY OKAFOR

BROWN DOG BOOKS

I dedicate this book to all the (in)fertility warriors out there, to all those that are silently suffering, to all who feel lost and without direction.
I want you to know, even if you can't see it yet…

Every journey has its purpose

Contents

Introduction

Flipping the Script on Infertility

That moment when you realise that having a baby is not as simple as you thought it would be is life-changing and earth-shattering and arrives in a single breath. It's like being thrown into a depth so unimaginable, so inconceivable, so... so difficult to explain to anyone who hasn't been through it themselves.

When fertility isn't a given, it is one of the most distressing experiences a woman can go through. I don't imagine I need to tell you that, you know it's distressing.

What is often talked and written about is the *physical* treatment of infertility – the treatments available, the ways that your fertility can be optimised. What tends to be discussed less frequently and openly is the emotional and psychological impact of infertility and its treatment. If this continues to be the norm, then we surely aren't talking about how to manage it either, which isn't helping any of us one little bit.

It's impossible to separate our physical body from our emotional selves and we know there is a defined mind-body connection. So, why is it that we tend to focus exclusively on treating the physical aspects of infertility?

In the pages which follow, I will illustrate why it is that mental health and emotional wellbeing are so important in the context of fertility. I'll explain some of the positive neuroscientific effects that come from managing our emotional wellbeing and mental health for ourselves as individuals.

As the Secondary Infertility warrior I came to consider myself to be in the past, I know only too well the emotional turmoil that comes with the battle. My own journey wasn't conventional by any means. I went through testing and was treated with Clomid. When that didn't work, I went into a deep depression and decided to walk away from assisted medical treatment altogether. Instead

Flipping the Script on Infertility

I spent years researching, and experimenting with, a host of holistic treatments, including acupuncture, functional nutrition and reflexology. At the same time, I retrained and qualified as an art therapist and counsellor, and this undoubtedly helped me to explore my emotional anguish in depth as well as giving me support that I so desperately needed.

I came to discover my 'ugly (beautiful) truths' that took me on an honest deep dive into me, into the things that have made me, and towards being open to accept truths that were hard and necessary to hear. Perhaps hearing my truths will trigger something in you. Perhaps if you are open to your own ugly (beautiful) truths, you too will gain deep insight into who you are at your core. Perhaps if you are willing, you will accept the truths that are hard and necessary to hear and make the intention to act on the practices that will bring about your own personal transformation.

I have structured the book so that you can journal along with me and I encourage you to do so. Journaling brings us the insight, clarity, and confidence in ourselves that we need to navigate our journeys through our lives on our own terms. It is empowering and supports us in taking charge of the choices we make, the treatments we choose, the options we decide not to pursue. It brings everything back within our control.

You know that emotional stress, anxiety, and depression are not conducive to 'good' fertility. We know and yet we don't know what to do about it. In writing this book, I want to share how you can control your emotions, how to shift your mindset to maximise your chances of getting pregnant with (or without) conventional treatment, and have a healthy pregnancy which leads to healthy motherhood. These also happen to be the tools we all need, not just on our fertility journeys, but in our lives.

Flipping the Script on Infertility

I could never have imagined navigating my own (in)fertility journey peacefully and calmly whilst also pursuing my passions, feeling fulfilled every day. Feeling this way feels so different from the turmoil and distress I was in that I no longer consider myself to be 'infertile', despite continuing to be so by medical definition. I share with you the tools that I have discovered on my personal journey, the tools that helped me to overcome the emotional distress, which I give to you in my Fertility Mindset Principles.

These pages hold the tools which enable us all as women going through challenges to support ourselves. The main thing I want you to know is – you will be okay. Whether or not your individual dreams of motherhood are realised, you will be okay. You are worthy of living in happiness. You are important. Becoming whole (mentally, emotionally, spiritually, and physically) is the key to becoming and being fully *YOU*.

'Infertility' and joy are not mutually exclusive. Challenging, perhaps. Impossible? No. You *can* decide to ditch your despair, overwhelm and pressure and choose happiness *today*. Choose to create your baby from a state of happiness. Choose happiness for yourself, your relationship, your family, and for your life. You can be the change that you want to see in this world now and in the future that you want for your children.

My story is your story is our story.
You can give yourself the best chance to become a mother.
You can give yourself the best chance to become the woman you aspire to be.

Prologue

Flipping the Script on Infertility

We tend to expect that people and things will make us happy. We look for fulfilment outside of ourselves. What I know is a baby will fill your womb for nine months before it becomes a person with whom you have to learn to forge a relationship, just as you would with anyone else. A baby cannot be responsible for your happiness. It's true that motherhood is filled with many, many amazing moments. Equally, there can be just as many dark moments that hide in the etiquette of our day-to-day social interactions.

When we don't have the something that we long to possess, that something appears wonderful to us in every single way. That baby bump looks extra gorgeous, that mini-me photo shoot extra cute. We tend to only see the happy, 'perfect' side of people's lives. If we were all privy to others' lives in all their imperfect glory, we would not have such idealised views, we would not judge our lives to be insufficient in comparison to another. Sometimes we might even catch ourselves saying that we long to experience the baby crying all night, the temper tantrums, the sibling fistfights. When we wish to experience someone's worst moments, what do we even really mean?

Motherhood is so idealised, and yet we rarely look closely at the statistics. The latest MBRRACE–UK report (MBRRACE-UK - Saving Lives, Improving Mothers' Care 2019) looked into the deaths of mums and babies in the UK between 2014 and 2016. Suicide was found to be the fifth most common cause of death during pregnancy and in the weeks following birth. However, it was the leading cause of death during the first year after pregnancy. What this tells us is that motherhood (like infertility) is complex, and when we focus our attention on the idealised mother, we fail mothers when they most need our help.

Infertility, while not idealised, has its own unfortunate statistics.

Flipping the Script on Infertility

A survey conducted in association with Middlesex University London, on the impact of fertility treatment on both women and men, found 42% of respondents experienced suicidal ideation (Fertility Network UK, 2017). Experiencing a failed cycle, or the loss of a pregnancy or attempting and not being able to carry a child at all, is a major loss. Depression and symptoms of post-traumatic stress are a natural response to grief, despair, anger and a whole host of emotions. However, untreated depression is a contributing factor of suicidal ideation and suicide itself.

Even with more up-to-date research, the full picture of 'infertile' life in all its complexity cannot be revealed with statistics. Approximately one in eight couples battle with infertility in the US (2006-2010 National Survey of Family Growth, CDC); it's around one in seven in the UK. (https://www.nhs.uk/conditions/infertility) However, this only represents the couples who seek treatment. There may be many hundreds of thousands of others suffering in silence with associated physical, mental and/or emotional health challenges.

Both infertility and motherhood are far more complex than they seem at face value. It's time to get real about women's mental health in the childbearing phase of life because lives are at risk. It isn't right that anyone should have to die because they feel they can't cope with the realities of their life.

We need more open and honest accounts of the realities of both mothers and infertility (primary or secondary) warriors (as well as women who are both mothers and considered 'infertile'), with starkly real and deeply honest accounts like my own which I have given voice to in this book.

I talk about what I know. I question what needs further consideration. This is not a how-to-get-through-IVF/IUI/ICSI (delete as appropriate) guide. Personally, I haven't found a 'get pregnant' method that worked for me at the time of writing. I haven't been through IVF. The information in this book doesn't equate to therapy, or to medical advice. It's important we each seek the advice appropriate to us as we need it. While it may take a little courage to reach out, please don't struggle in silence when the following services can help:

NHS
Contact your GP. Talk to your GP about getting counselling on the NHS. This will give you an opportunity to explore your feelings around fertility more generally and is something you can do on your own or with your partner.

British Infertility Counselling Association (BICA):
www.bica.net
BICA is the only professional counselling association for infertility counsellors and counselling in the UK.

Ectopic Pregnancy Foundation:
www.ectopicpregnancy.co.uk
Helpline, information, forum.

Ectopic Pregnancy Trust: www.ectopic.org.uk
Helpline providing support and information for women and families affected by an ectopic pregnancy.

Fertility Friends: www.fertilityfriends.co.uk
Infertility and fertility support leading infertility community in the UK with members at every stage of their journey. Infertility, adoption, parenting, after infertility and moving on.

Flipping the Script on Infertility

Fertility Network UK: www.fertilitynetworkuk.org
Free and impartial support, advice, information and understanding for anyone affected by fertility issues.

Miscarriage Association: www.miscarriageassociation.org.uk
Information and support for people affected by the loss of a baby in pregnancy.

Samaritans: www.samaritans.org
Call free on 116 123, 24 hours a day, 365 days a year.

Part One: Infertility Sucks*

* Definition – To suck (verb): to be very bad or unpleasant
[to put it very mildly]

Seven little words...

There's a moment, a simple moment, when your life changes. You can't go back. You can't unknow. You can't pretend that the moment didn't happen, and you can't ever forget it.

In my life-changing moment, seven little words stuck to my ribs, reverberated around in my head, fell clumsily and incredulously from my lips as I repeated them aloud, nonsensically attempting to make sense of them. They wouldn't sink in. They wouldn't disappear. They just bounced around inside me, silently and defiantly hinting that they meant something. Like they were noisily whispering, 'Pay attention, Kezia.'

I could do nothing less than ask myself what it would mean if I did?

There are so many words, so many moments like this in our lives, where we know the truth lies deep inside us and yet, because of the pain they inflict, there are just two choices; evolve, or ignore.

Ultimately, to ignore will mean we repeat and repeat our habitual cycles. As a therapist, I see this in so many individuals' repeated patterns, recurrent bad choices. I see their unconscious reactions to events that they cannot realise, acknowledge, or accept yet, if they ever will.

To evolve brings a realisation, an acknowledgement, and an acceptance of a something that can no longer be ignored.

Flipping the Script on Infertility

In my seven-little-words moment, it was painfully clear to me that this was something, that if it were something I chose to accept, would change my world. Like any life-changing moment, it would be important to understand what brought me to it.

The something was a longing, a terrible, all-consuming longing to give my son a sibling.

This longing took me on a journey so dark and so painful, it took me into a void of nothingness, where only deep and desperate despair lived.

The 'experts' called it 'Unexplained Secondary Infertility'[1].

I called it misery.

Like any void, in time my 'infertility' became an imploding black hole which threatened to consume me bit by tiny bit. I busied myself in devouring every little morsel of information, every suggestion, every hack, every fertility-boosting fact that I could – I became nothing short of obsessive. I became the epitome of self-loathing; it oozed from my every pore, a wild and personal stink of desperation and longing. I hated myself in a way that only I could. I was vicious and unrelentless in my attacks on myself.

I was 'useless'.

I was 'a failure'.

I was... immensely sad. So, so, so immensely sad. Yet it felt like no one could see it or feel it but me. Perhaps they did. I know I certainly didn't want anyone to see it. I was hiding in plain sight, behind my anger, my frustration, behind my desperate determination.

I was a mother who was desperate to be a mother... again. No one around me could understand it, I couldn't understand it, and

---

1 Secondary Infertility is defined as the inability to become pregnant or to carry a pregnancy successfully after previous success in delivering a child

to my rational mind, it made little sense, even to me. I already had what so many others want.

So, off I set on an indescribable 'journey' to have tests and procedures, to take fertility-boosting medication, to consult with gynaecologists, acupuncturists, nutritionists, reflexologists and dieticians. Yet, after four years, nothing.

In a final, last-ditch swing of my bat, I was referred to an osteopath, and I went along to yet another appointment, albeit reluctantly. I wasn't hopeful that this one would prove any different to all those I'd attended before. In this one-hour assessment, I detailed my painful, four-year history again. This time, the response changed my life, changed me forever when the osteopath gave voice to those seven little words:

'Perhaps the problem is in your unconscious.'

Waiting on that line...

When you experience infertility, you do get used to waiting. In fact, it feels as though your life is on a tightrope – you are just about balancing, just about coping, and resisting slipping into oblivion, just about. Waiting is the name of the game; waiting for your turn in the waiting room, waiting for that second line that might never appear, waiting... to become a mum.

It's difficult to describe how infertility consumed me looking back. My every thought, every day for more than four years was dominated by despair, desperation, and a terrible, deep, omnipresent sadness. I was empty and broken, and even though I would say this about my physical body, at some level I knew I also meant that I was broken both spiritually and emotionally. Something was missing.

I spent a long time searching for answers. I think that is what happens when you are told your infertility is 'unexplained'. It leaves you bereft, scrabbling around in the dark, attempting to make sense of it, when there *is* no sense to be made. It was incredible to me that in these times, when we are seriously attempting passenger trips to the moon and to Mars, that we have no real understanding of the female reproductive system. Why does it take so many visits to the doctor to be taken seriously that something is wrong? Why does it take seven years (on average) to diagnose endometriosis? (Endomentriosis-uk.org) Why must women go through so much chronic pain to be told its 'just how menstruation is for some women'? Women deserve better treatment than this in the 21st century.

The inability to conceive or to carry a pregnancy to full term after doing so without difficulty previously is the definition of secondary infertility (SI). SI numbers are far higher than you might expect, and they're rising. A US study revealed that, in 1995, 1.8 million women suffered from secondary infertility; in 2006, it was 3.3 million. SI now accounts for six in ten infertility cases. (theguardian.com, 2010)

It's a commonly held view that if a woman can have one child, then she can have another. This is (ironically) a misconception. It's a misconception that I shared until I couldn't have another child. That's when I, and perhaps you too, were unceremoniously initiated into the harsh reality of SI. Those with Primary Infertility[2] may think that someone with SI is, by comparison, lucky, and in some ways, rightly so. I feel so incredibly lucky to have my son and yet my longing for his sibling was ever-present.

I used to be fixated on the ever-growing age gap between my son and his future sibling. This can be another tormenting aspect of Secondary Infertility. My husband and I had dreams about having three children close in age. I wanted a three-year gap between my kids. I'm not entirely sure why, it was a pretty arbitrary goal. It became pure anguish as my son grew, and every birthday milestone he reached felt like I was failing him. The story I was telling myself about this was limiting my reality. My son will of course be an

---

2   Primary Infertility refers to couples who have not become pregnant after at least 1 year having sex without using birth control methods

amazing sibling irrespective of the age gap. I wasn't able to see that. The only consideration in my field of vision at the time was that other people had *their* children close together.

There was a point at which I happened to come across a simple comment on a random blog and it had a profound effect on me: 'Fear not the age gap, love transcends the details.'

Every family is unique; the passage of time can never equate to love. My focus on the arbitrary counting of the years (months, Christmases, birthdays, anniversaries, cycles...) used to cause me inordinate distress. So much energy was spent counting the passage of time. Because infertility was all about the time invested. Time to calculate when I might be ovulating, or where we just might be in nine months' time, so many aspects of life put on hold or even ignored while I played the 'What if..?' game.

It's ridiculously hard to let all of that go, all that time invested, all of those years of 'trying', so hard in fact, that you just *keep on trying*. I can't tell you how many times I said, 'No more. I can't do this anymore!' and then, in the very next breath admitted, 'Oh, I don't know... But what if?'

This is the essence of the internal conflict we go through with infertility. You might get to a point where you've gone so far you don't want to give up, yet you just aren't sure how much further (if at all) you might have to go. This keeps you stuck, unmoving, in the worst kind of limbo. Months and years become a blur, as your cycles just repeat and repeat and repeat. I called it the life unlived.

Life is precious, even if we are not entirely sure why *ours* is, or what our individual purpose might be. To squander life seems morally inexcusable. We all know of someone who may wish for one more year and wasting our years on 'What ifs' feels reprehensible. So, on we go, stuck in the most painful game of tug of war with ourselves.

When your every thought is consumed by what you perceive to be your infertility, it starts to define you and your every interaction. Your conversations are defined by it, it's all you think about, it's all the information you consume. You feed your desperate need for fertility, a need which is never satisfied, so you afford more and more of your energy to it. You become the very embodiment of 'infertile' – you don't just have it, you *are* it. I've learned as a therapist that when we overidentify with a physical condition or experience, there comes a point when we need to separate ourselves (and our very identity) from it. Through therapy, we learn when we need to *integrate our challenges into the self*, and when we need to *separate them from the self*. For me, this was incredibly pertinent in terms of my 'infertility'.

I had work to do to enable me to move from the me that was fused with or *defined by* my infertility to the me that now *has* infertility and is detached from it. Infertility was not all that I was, it's not all that I am. This shift in perspective required me to move from an 'I'm infertile' story to one in which 'I have infertility' in order to go a step further and completely disassociate myself from it. It doesn't serve me, and it won't serve you in any way to even 'have' it. 'Infertility' is no longer a theme in my thoughts about myself. I no longer use that word to describe my experience or where I'm at.

The most important thing is to know that your 'infertility' does not define you either. It is not who you are, and it certainly does not define what you're capable of.

When 'unexplained' feels like unenlightened...

Officially, 'unexplained infertility' occurs when standard fertility testing, such as scans, tubal patency tests and semen analysis all fail to reveal a cause for the infertility. Approximately one in four 'infertile' couples will experience infertility which is deemed 'unexplained'. (www.nhs.uk)

It's a frustrating 'diagnosis' as it just means that while there probably is a reason, medics can't tell you what it is.

While our trusty search engines and digital assistants can give us answers to any and every question in seconds, we can't seem to expect the same from medicine. We assume that the medical profession must know everything there is to know about reproduction. It's frustrating to discover that we don't and that there isn't even an answer to why we don't have this knowledge in the 21st century.

Unexplained infertility plunges you into a black hole where you find yourself asking, 'Now what?' and 'What exactly am I meant to do with this information?' I felt like a dog chasing its tail, so desperate was my need to find the answers, so tormented by exasperation, so determined that there *must be* an answer.

Unexplained infertility doesn't mean fewer options, though.

Flipping the Script on Infertility

There are currently about forty ways to treat 'infertility' (Harvard Health Publishing, 2009), from conventional methods, including advice about the timing of intercourse and the prescription of pharmacological (drug) therapy to promote ovulation or prevent miscarriages, through to surgery to repair reproductive organs, or even more advanced assisted reproductive technology.

None of these make unexplained infertility any less frustrating.

Fertility experts once suggested that only about half of all infertility cases had a physical origin; the rest were unexplained and/or the result of psychosomatic problems, specifically in women. In contrast, more recent research indicates that most cases of infertility can be attributed to a physiological cause in either the man or the woman. (Harvard Health Publishing, 2009)

What if some cases of unexplained infertility *are* psychosomatic, rather than physiological, in origin? Why is it that experts in the field no longer think so? There have been many and various changes in modern society, including the trend that couples tend to start their families later in life and that technology now drives our culture with staggering advances, including in terms of medical technology. IVF is now more widely available than ever before. None of this changes the fact that our bodies respond to the ways in which we think, feel, and act. Our thoughts, feelings, beliefs, and attitudes can affect, positively or negatively, our biological functioning. In short, **our minds affect how healthy our bodies are.**

Similarly, what we do to our physical bodies (what we eat, how much we exercise, even how much attention we pay to our posture) can impact our mental state either positively or negatively. Fertility/infertility must surely exist within, and be influenced by, this complex interrelationship between our minds and our bodies.

It's important to note that 'mind' is not synonymous with

'brain'. Our minds consist of mental states which incorporate thoughts, emotions, beliefs, attitudes, and images. The brain is the hardware which allows us to experience these mental states. Mental states can be fully conscious or unconscious. We can have emotional reactions to situations without being aware of why we are reacting. Different mental states can affect our biological functioning positively or negatively. Our nervous, endocrine, and immune systems all share a common chemical language which allows constant communication between the mind and body via messengers which include hormones and neurotransmitters.

Neurological pathways connect the parts of the brain which process emotions with the spinal cord, muscles, cardiovascular system, and digestive tract. This is why major life events, stressors, or emotions can trigger physical symptoms, like the butterflies we may feel in our stomachs when we feel nervous, or when our hearts feel like they are pounding out of our chests when we are under intense stress.

These inter-related systems establish the mind-body connection which influences the maintenance of health or the development of disease. Emotions like anxiety can trigger increased levels of stress hormones, and this, in turn, may suppress our immune systems and increase the risk of our susceptibility to infections.

Around three hundred years ago, virtually every system of medicine throughout the world treated the mind and body as a whole. During the 17th century, the Western world began to view the mind and body as two distinct entities whereby the body was regarded as a machine, complete with replaceable, independent parts, with no connection whatsoever to the mind. This perspective definitely reaped considerable benefit as it became the foundation for advances in surgery, trauma care, pharmaceuticals, and other areas of medicine. However, it also greatly reduced scientific inquiry into the emotional and spiritual life of humans and downplayed our innate ability to heal.

In the 20th century, this view began to change. Researchers began to study the mind-body connection and to demonstrate, scientifically, the myriad complex links between body and mind. Many mind-body therapies, including yoga, meditation techniques, hypnosis, and creative arts therapies, focus on us becoming more conscious of our mental states and using this awareness to guide our thoughts in healthier and less destructive directions.

What if, by failing to treat the mind, we are reducing the effectiveness of our fertility treatment outcomes? What if, by treating our bodies in isolation, we consume drugs and hormones that are unnecessary as our minds already produce what we need when mind and body function well together?

Fundamentally, is the answer to our struggles with infertility, and our emotional challenges in particular, to be found within our own minds and the ways in which we think?

Our fertility issues may not just lie in our wombs.

You can treat your whole self, give yourself permission to feel whatever it is you feel – no guilt, no shame. You can take back your power, take control of your life, how you think and how you feel. Ask yourself if you want to stay stuck in the way you are feeling or if you want how you feel to change. Your health and wellbeing are yours and yours alone.

We have the power to change our thoughts and pay attention to our feelings.

Flipping the Script on Infertility

Do you journal? I invite you to journal as you go along on this journey with me and have created these journal sections for your reflections, with prompts and questions for you to respond to. I have structured the book in this way to allow for you to start your personal deep self-reflection work. It is only natural that things from your own life experience will come up as you read through these pages and having the space to think deeply on these experiences will greatly benefit your process of self-understanding and change. As a practice journaling is a good way to help you to stop, take a step back and reflect on yourself, giving clarity to your thoughts and feelings. Allow yourself to write down whatever is on your mind or whatever you are feeling without judgement or fear.

JOURNAL EXERCISE
- Does it seem possible that you can heal yourself?
- Are you able to open your mind to consider a kind of healing which extends beyond your physical body?

Education, education, education...

My infertility diagnosis taught me that I needed to unlearn a lot of what I thought I knew.

I had to unlearn what I thought about my body. I had to learn that fertility starts in the mind.

Why is it that education about sex and reproduction tends to be rooted in prevention and fear?

My personal experience of education was drawn mainly from the single-sex girls' secondary school I was a pupil at. I remember one horrifying, so-called sex education lesson. Our Religious Education teacher, an ex-nun, outlined graphic details of sexually transmitted diseases (STIs) and seemed determined to scare us into crossing our legs forever more. In Biology lessons, a video was played, while our male science teacher looked rather sheepish and uncomfortable. A fair bit of my sex education came from the pages of a teen magazine which was graphic and at times almost pornographic in its descriptions of sex and sexual fantasy. Even in a glossy magazine whose audience was young women and teenage girls, everything seemed to be influenced by the male perspective. Back in primary school, all of the girls in my class were taken to the hall for a talk with the local (female) GP. We sat around in a private circle as she talked to us about periods and what to expect. I remember how intimate and caring an atmosphere it was. Just us girls sharing practical information about being girls. Back then it was so hard to access real, factual information about women, written by women for women. Now we have *so* much information at our fingertips, it can be overwhelming, and too much information can lead to misinformation.

When you are considered 'infertile', it's safe to say that none of your knowledge about sex, fertility and conception comes from formal education. Finding myself in the eye of a fertility challenge storm made me become an armchair "expert" in reproduction. So much of this process remains a mystery that so many of us just take for granted.

It has led me to wonder if there is a patriarchal conspiracy which keeps female biology and fertility under wraps. Does the patriarchy benefit from preventing women from an understanding of who they innately are, based on an informed knowledge of their biology? In Western capitalist society, does it serve the patriarchy for women to be unaware that their intrinsic value is in their very being, not in their doing. As the popular quote goes, we are human *beings,* not human *doings,* after all.

There is, indisputably, power in knowledge. Perhaps it is just a symptom of our preoccupation with progress and with technological endeavour that we've lost sight of our individual power. We are certainly not taught about what it means to be a human, to be our whole, holistic selves; this learning seems to have been lost along the way in our 200,000-year history. The most powerful computer (with its one hundred billion neuron cells and one million billion synapse connections) known to man/woman is, after all, the human brain.

Yet our universal collective thought processes tend to be filled with self-doubt, fear, worry, and *lack* of every kind. We torture ourselves that we are not enough – not smart enough, pretty enough, rich enough, skinny enough, strong enough, not enough... enough. When we hear, 'Get yourself a good education, get a good job, then get married and have kids,' they sum up an entire life in a single second. Why do our stories have to 'end' with having children? Why is such a vague and limited lifepath considered the norm?

It seems as though we are all meant to have life all figured out by the age of thirty; no wonder so many of us feel like complete failures when we achieve none of the above by twenty-nine. No wonder we feel we should do more, *be* more. Yet, evolution has hard-wired us to fit in, to belong – to the family, to the group, to the community. We follow accepted paths because that's what we are taught to do. Many of us subscribe to those paths which lead us to jobs, partners, and then wanting to have kids.

We learn that there is a time limit to this latter wish. There are also rules: we mustn't be too young, nor too old; we mustn't just have one, nor have them too far apart. Where do these checklists come from? Who determines them? And why, oh why, do we buy in to them? No matter how much progress there is in the world around us, we continue to buy into old systems of how life 'should' be lived. We experience so much anxiety when our lives do not sit recognisably within the status quo, perhaps not least when 'infertility' enters our lives and disrupts our 'natural' course of events.

We need to unlearn so we can learn.

My formal education certainly gave me the impression that I could get pregnant when I wanted to. It made me think I could get pregnant on any day of the month, that I could have as many children as I wanted. My thinking was based on the universal assumptions like this that so many of us make. There isn't a woman struggling with (in)fertility out there who hasn't had to *really* learn about conception, her mechanics, the reality of what happens physiologically and biologically, the how, the when, and even the likelihood of what needs to happen for pregnancy to be the outcome.

Life, and becoming a mother, is about learning and unlearning.

I've had to unlearn what I thought about myself, what I thought about others and what I thought about the world. Every day, I'm unlearning what I thought it would be to live a life I desired, what I thought it would be to run a business, what I thought I needed to get through each day, what I thought peace would look like...

I had to unlearn a mindset that had kept me stuck in my repeated patterns, in my habitual and limited thinking, in maladaptive behaviours. Therapy brings learning, learning brings understanding; **un**learning means you learn to replace what isn't working with something new that brings about change. We reject our old mindset and replace it with new ways of thinking. We unlearn.

Unlearning is transformative. We get to rethink who we are and could be, to rewrite our stories from tales of woe to legends of sheroes, we get to reclaim our power and realise our own destinies.

When coming to terms with 'infertility', you are in a process of becoming. Who or what you become is yours to determine. When you embrace your becoming, you no longer judge or hate yourself, instead you will show love for yourself as you undergo your process of learning/unlearning, becoming/unbecoming every day. We learn, unlearn, and relearn, we think we've got it, we relapse.

Change is inevitable, sometimes scary, but inevitable. We can welcome it or allow it to sneak up on us. The power we have within us is the power to change our minds. We can change our mindsets, our thoughts, our beliefs. **We can change our minds, and thus change our realities, change our lives.**

I embrace change, because it is my nature to always be looking ahead (see five house moves in ten years and countless related and unrelated projects for details). When I look ahead, I can see that good things always come out of a period of change or growth, even if it is a learning of what *not* to do, even when change feels costly at the time.

Nothing good comes of remaining in our comfort zones other than a pressure to keep things exactly as they are – and this is impossible. Change heralds the start of new chapters – change is exactly what *you* seek, yet perhaps the change you need is not the one you think it is.

*Motherhood **is** change.*

It is a becoming, a transition from one to two (or more). This is a change you dearly hope and wish for. Fertility/infertility is a period of transition into motherhood and into becoming who you are destined to be, whether or not the outcome is that you become a parent.

JOURNAL EXERCISE
- What do you need to learn, unlearn, and relearn?
- What changes have occurred in you since being considered to have or diagnosed with 'infertility'?

When failing feels like a fall...

If you are like I was, you feel like a failure every day, every month, every cycle, every period, every big fat negative. Constantly failing.

While it might be a hard lesson to learn, we *can* learn to see that 'failure' is just our own perception of events.

In fact, success or failure is all in our minds, it is just the experiences that we give meaning to, judge good or bad, success or failure.

What if there *were* no judgement? What if we no longer judged ourselves or our experiences? Habits definitely die hard; for many of us the need to judge feels so inherent to our being that it's almost like breathing.

All judgement does is keep you from seeing the potential in your experiences. It fuels that critical voice in your mind and gives it more and more ammunition.

Two of the 'failures' of my life left scars which ran deep. They have taken work to find peace with. The first was my struggle with my 'infertility'. The second, a career path that 'never got started'.

I left university with a photography degree, ready to conquer the world. I had dreams of travelling and working on amazing photoshoots with famous models for big fashion magazines. It wasn't that I wasn't determined. My dream felt massive and when something feels massive, it overwhelms us and when we are overwhelmed, it is easy to be paralysed by inaction. I found myself lurching from dead-end job to dead-end job, wondering how I'd ended up there, with those people. I was lost long before I consciously realised. It was a crushing hurt when I did, a hurt so deep and seismic that I didn't talk about it. It rocked me to my core and made me question every aspect of who I thought I was. When my photography dream died, I had no others. I felt too small and insignificant to chase my dreams.

Looking back now, if I'd taken away my judgement, if I'd released the idea of 'failure', I can acknowledge this experience as a necessary period which I learned valuable lessons from. I can see that it has brought me to where I am today. I can see now that what I *do* in life *is* important to me. Without a clear sense of direction or purpose, I tend to drift off course and wander through life beating myself up. I have a tendency to dwell on what might have been. 'Infertility' exacerbated this tendency in me. It's easy for me to see now that periods like this had a definite purpose. They showed me what it is like to live life, absent of meaning.

The future can be anxiety-inducing at the best of times, especially when we want something to happen, but we're not sure how or if it will. It can become crippling and it can prevent us from chasing our dreams or fulfilling our desires. How often do we hear people say things like, 'I had the chance to...' or, 'I could have been...' Failure hurts. Most of us will go to great lengths to avoid it. Even if that means holding ourselves back from pursuing our true ambitions.

Anticipatory anxiety is a term for when you feel overwhelmed by a fear of what might happen, even if it's the kind of success we crave, like becoming pregnant. Our minds tend to jump ahead to anticipate all of the things that *could* go wrong. For me, it was knowing what I wanted to happen and feeling daunted by the huge gulf between where I was and where I wanted to be that was paralysing at times. Its enormity would inevitably see me fall into a chasm of anxiety and deem myself a failure.

Why are we so fearful of success? We are so scared to fail that we sometimes don't even try, we stay small, within our comfort zones and the confines of what we know.

This is because our brains are designed to keep us alive. Our neurological wiring favours what we know so that we can respond swiftly and efficiently to any threat and survive. The more we step into the unfamiliar, the more we feel fear, and worry.

It's also natural that we project our past experiences – not least our failures – onto our futures, 'fortune-telling' stories to ourselves by jumping to negative conclusions or predicting poor outcomes from our efforts. We do this when we tell ourselves, 'It isn't going to happen this month,' or 'I just know that test won't be positive.' In reality, we can all see this kind of thinking for what it is – an example of cognitive distortion or irrational thought process which skews our perception of reality in negative ways. It significantly perpetuates psychopathological states such as depression and anxiety. These are maladaptive thought patterns which are difficult to identify when they are beyond our conscious awareness. Rather than challenge such thoughts, we end up living predictable futures – where we do what we have always done, feel what we always feel and think what we always think.

When we redefine failure, we see that it is inevitable, and that no one has ever died from failure itself – businesses continue, exams can be retaken, something else can be tried, there may be other treatment cycles. We are able to keep going because there may be a different outcome next time. We don't die from it, we just continue on, hampered by it.

We need to unlearn 'failure', to *accept* that it is inevitable, and continue, equipped with the learning it has given us. We need to learn to analyse 'failure', to study it, learn from it and ask ourselves what we could do differently. With our 'infertility', we can reframe the perceived 'failures' of previous cycles (you *can*). Like me, you can come to see our 'failures' differently, so you don't continue to limit yourself to living a predictable future.

Instead of seeing every cycle that didn't end in pregnancy as a failure, I instead began to see it as a 'not yet'. I focused hard on the positives (I was having periods and periods were a good sign that my body was working). I worked hard on my relationship with outcomes and endpoints. My goal, I thought, was to become pregnant. In reality, it was just another step along my life path. In reality, there are no endpoints, just forks in the road. Sometimes your road just keeps on forking. Where there is no failure, there is just more opportunity.

If we see every disappointment as 'failure', we are focusing solely on the outcome. Every disappointing cycle will become your every failure. Your ability to unlearn 'failure' will have positive effects in many other areas of your life, your job, your relationships, your finances, your physical health as a whole. Perfectionism is problematic and dictates that every challenge we face becomes a need for us to prove ourselves over and over again. We demand of us that we prove that we can get pregnant, prove that we're worthy of love, prove our worth as a wife, partner, as a woman. It's time we let ourselves off that particularly perfect hook. It's time to see every difficulty you face as an opportunity to learn more about who you are and want you want. In time, the forks in your road will become the pivots that you welcome.

Flipping the Script on Infertility

To achieve change in your habits, your mind and body also go through change. Your inner world needs to change to evolve with each pivot that you make.

When sex is more mission than missionary...

'Infertility' combined with sex, intimacy and marriage do not make for happy bedfellows.

Making a baby isn't necessarily much fun. It can mean intercourse planned/timed by your fertile window, it can mean checking your calendar, tracking your ovulation, examining your cervical mucus and monitoring your basal body temperature. It's having an argument instead of having sex, it's being angry and then having sex anyway, it's going to bed upset because you know you've missed your window. It's not intimacy. It's not how you thought you would make your baby.

It can be the least fun that anyone anywhere has ever had in the bedroom. It's pressure. The pressure, both spoken and unspoken, is that there is a goal and that goal is to make a baby. The baby becomes a holy grail that you're both chasing, and you begin to feel unworthy; you just can't quite grasp it.

It can be disappointment. Sometimes it feels easier not to have sex, rather than feel that you have failed at sex. Because that's what it can feel like – when your period arrives again or you take another negative test, you can feel you have failed at sex once again. Failed as a couple once again. Failed as a woman once again. How can something so natural become so difficult, so *un*natural?

Making a baby is like taking on (another) full-time job; it's constant and you're never off the clock.

The strain this puts on a relationship can be immense. Although my husband and I were in it together, my despair felt greater than his. There were times when he would bring up the subject of our 'infertility', and sometimes he would get upset, though mostly he just seemed to deal with it better. We constantly considered whether we should keep 'trying' or not. The milestones of life always brought us both back up short, to imagining and hoping for the large family we dreamed of.

I always shouldered the blame. I felt like it was my fault. I felt it was my cross to bear. He didn't like seeing me in such despair. Even though a couple go through 'infertility' together, it is somehow a very solitary, and very personal, kind of anguish.

'Infertility' can be challenging in this way. While you, as an individual, never imagined going through it, it is also not something that you, as a couple, ever imagined facing either. In your loved-up, honeymoon phase of romance, you probably talked about having kids together, took each other's life-goals-inventory to make sure that you were both on the same page. It's unlikely that you talked about how having children might be a struggle for you. As a couple, you tend to come unprepared for 'infertility', armed with no joint plan for what it is you might want, or would do in the event that you endure 'infertility' or end up childless.

As a couple, you just move forward from the start, hoping it will happen. It's not uncommon for one member of a couple to want to seek treatment more than the other. It's not uncommon that one of you will be happy to live life as a couple without children and to make a fulfilling life together. It can be hard to have these conversations once you are already stressed about not conceiving. Minor, incidental comments can cause conflict and resentment and result in a sense that one of you doesn't want it as badly as the other. It will be difficult to watch a partner going through torment, and difficult not to feel that this wasn't what you imagined or wanted for your life together.

Relationships are difficult at the best of times. They take commitment, compromise, forgiveness, and... effort. It takes an enormous level of effort to, as a couple, go forward after an infertility diagnosis, to keep on trying, to keep on hoping.

What you risk losing in your quest to make a family, is you as a couple. Falling in love was the easy part. Deciding to start a family was the easy part. The challenge is to remember that you were a couple first, before 'infertility' ever became a part of your reality.

In my relationship, talking about the effects of 'infertility' on us as individuals and on us as a couple was incredibly challenging. Sex is important in any relationship, perhaps even more so when trying to conceive. The conflict that can arise around timing, pressure, expectation, performance, outcome is immense.

Sex can easily become a job. It's important not to have sex just when it's your fertile window, or regimentally every other day. It's important to make it a priority just when the moment takes you, when you're in the mood. It's important to make time for it again, like you did in those early days when you made an effort for each other. The fact is that sex is good for your relationship.

Even more challenging is the 'What if we don't have children, what then?' question. It is the most important conversation you can, and need to, have as a couple. It mustn't be avoided. Find the courage to share your concerns. Boldly build your life together according to your rules, your dreams, the ones that you create together. When your life paths veer off course, find the courage to feel the fear, to re-evaluate your joint dreams and take new and unexpected directions, together.

I learned that I feel stronger when my husband and I walk together holding hands. I learned that life together does not have to look like other people's lives. It wasn't, and isn't, anyone else's life that I wanted so I decided to stop looking at them. Our lives cannot be determined by what others are doing or what others have. I want the extraordinary for my marriage, as you no doubt do for yours. This might mean living life according to different rules – your relationship is the absolute foundation of your future family.

JOURNAL EXERCISE

- Are you able to have conversations about what being considered 'infertile' feels like with your partner?
- Do you both share your fears and feelings openly?
- What are you most grateful to your partner for?

Black women are fertile.
Aren't they?

Black women suffer 'infertility' too. It's true.

While 'infertility' is estimated to affect around 12% of women under the age of 44, black women are twice as likely to struggle than white women, yet only about 8% speak to their doctor or seek medical help compared to 15% of their white counterparts. (cdc. gov, 2014)

I am one of the 8%.

Whatever your race or background, facing 'infertility' is hard – arguably harder still as a woman who is black or from an ethnic minority (BAME). It is often considered taboo in some ethnic cultures to talk about infertility. I'm of West Indian (Caribbean) heritage and in my culture, it's not openly talked about; which makes it feel like it's not supposed to be an issue. Sadly, this is not the reality.

Sadder still is that this makes it incredibly isolating. Seeking treatment is then also loaded with shame.

While 'infertility' may not present as a serious health condition of life-threatening proportions at face value, it can be detrimental to health and result in depression, distress, anxiety, and even suicidal ideation. Medical infertility may also be caused by other reproductive health conditions such as fibroids, PCOS, endometriosis, or even sexually transmitted diseases, such as pelvic inflammatory disease.

Deeply rooted beliefs within BAME families and communities are likely to lead to women being (or certainly *feeling* they are being) discriminated against or ostracised due to their struggle to conceive and bear a child. As with every other physical and mental health condition, 'infertility' is also subject to racial disparities which stem from the racism and implicit bias systemic in our economic, educational, health and medical structures.

What's even more frustrating as a Black British woman, is that all of the – albeit limited – research and understanding of this issue is drawn from studies on data from *African-American* women, and not black women and ethnic minorities in the UK. It is a very personal – potentially universal for others like me – frustration. When I looked for others who looked like me in support groups or during treatment, there was no one who came from where I did, no one who lived a similar life to me. It was incredibly isolating. I knew I wasn't the only one; I just couldn't find anyone talking about being 'infertile'.

In recent times, we have heard (famous) black (American) women speaking up about their struggles with diagnoses of infertility, women like Michelle Obama and Gabrielle Union, and yet I wonder what difference this makes to the rest of us? Perhaps we view these women differently because of their celebrity, it's certainly not the same as talking to a friend or colleague who's been through it. Perhaps these women are just too far removed from our day-to-day reality to really have an impact on those who may be struggling with their fertility in the here and now. There is also an element of being distanced when it is discussed after the fact. When you're on the other side of it all, people only get to see where you are at now, rather than how you experienced it as you were going through it.

There is topical and widespread discussion on why representation matters, especially now, in the wake of the global Black Lives Matter (BLM) movement. In fertility treatment, representation definitely feels as though it is flying under the radar. It is indisputable that most fertility treatment marketing images depict white women, white babies, white families, and perpetuate the notion that 'infertility' only affects white women.

Is this because there is unconscious bias from fertility clinics who assume white women will, economically, be more likely to invest? A systemic perception that there are those who can afford treatment and those who can't, would also mean there is a class/wealth bias issue in fertility treatment.

In fact, there are many, many black women and women of ethnic minorities who have the means, financial and otherwise, to access treatment. If numbers of BAME women accessing services are low, why bother marketing treatments to them at all? While this short-sightedness is undoubtedly a missed opportunity, it's hard to ignore the part that socioeconomics plays here. The cost of accessing fertility treatment is a deterrent for many women, regardless of origin. However, this does not mean that we can continue to accept that the full spectrum of fertility awareness, education, treatment and care isn't equitably available to all women.

The mainstream media and the marketing of fertility treatments can also be so much better. When you can't find yourself represented in fertility treatment ads, all it does it add to your shame. It makes you think (even more) that there must be something wrong with *you* because you can't identify anyone who looks like you who is going through fertility challenges too. Feeling different is so horribly isolating. The problem is not in marketing alone, though – if black women are twice as likely to have fertility issues, why are only 8% accessing services? (cdc.gov, 2014) In my experience, childless black women over thirty-five often have concerns about their fertility and admit that they don't feel they know much about it.

It is a universal trend that many women are waiting longer to start families – for numerous reasons, careers, money, relationships. Black and ethnic minority women are not so remarkably different in this respect. What *is* different is the openness with which problems with health are discussed in black communities. It's due to a generational epidemic of 'not discussing', which millennial black women (and men) are now finding the courage to challenge and actively bring awareness to. Mental health issues are treated similarly; slowly, this is beginning to change as awareness of generational trauma grows.

That said, the silence around infertility in the black community in particular, is deafening. Perhaps it's not perceived to be a significant problem. Yet silence changes nothing, because in silence there is an assumption that no one is suffering and if no one is suffering then there is no problem.

Personally, I couldn't be, or have been, silent if I tried. That's not to say that I shouted it from the rooftops; I was selective about who I confided in. However, if anyone asked me about having more children, I was always open and honest in my responses. I would not and could not be ashamed of my truth. I was feeling a lot of things: sad, angry, despairing, desperate. I was searching for answers and for me, this meant searching for the language I could use to communicate my story; silence was never a part of that. I grew up in a family in which it was considered normal to talk about ailments, possibly because my grandmother was a nurse in the NHS and always had an antidote (or failing that, an anecdote) for *every* condition.

The trauma that black people carry is heavy. We have worries, unique to the black community, that the majority of the population rarely, if ever, have to consider. We fear how we will be treated as individuals because of the colour of our skin. We also fear how the children that we birth will be treated, what disadvantages they will be at, what associated challenges we will face as parents. It doesn't stop us from wanting children. It *does* add a further layer of anxiety to the existing stress, fear, and doubt that members of our race experience in their day-to-day lives.

We – all women, all men, all couples – experiencing fertility issues are desperately trying to make sense of who we are and what we're going through. Difficulties with fertility don't discriminate. The structural inequalities that surround women's health, and infertility in particular, do. We need inclusivity.

JOURNAL EXERCISE
- What are your experiences of feeling excluded during your fertility journey?
- What would you wish were different for other women going through it?

To IVF or not to IVF...

Your individuality, your very *humanness* can feel very much absent when you are undergoing fertility investigations and treatments. The medical model of infertility is so sad and sterile and devoid of spirit. Couples with physical causes for their infertility need medical assistance and rightly so. Yet I wonder why IVF isn't more effective than it is. Between 2014 and 2016, the percentage of treatments that resulted in live births was 23% for women aged 35-37. (nhs.uk/ivf) At age 35, most women have a 15-20% chance of conceiving naturally in any given month. (Eagleson H, parents. com) This is a low return on investment, especially when you consider the associated price tag.

I wonder about the popular narrative that fertility declines at the age of thirty-five. It certainly causes panic and stress. I'd suggest that the stress of desperately trying to conceive while being told we're getting 'too old' is more likely to have an impact on our fertility than our actual physical age. I also know that I'm not a doctor. We must remember that, while the fertility industry is helping to make families possible, it is also an industry led by 'Big Money'. The global market is expected to reach 37.7 billion USD by 2027 (grandviewresearch.com, 2020) and the U.S. fertility market 15.4 billion USD by 2023, up from almost seven billion USD in 2017. (Kowitt B, 2020) Baby-making is clearly BIG business.

Flipping the Script on Infertility

Back in 2010, the World Health Organization (WHO) estimated that infertility rates had remained relatively unchanged in the previous decade. (Warren-Gash Dr, 2013) The WHO website now states that infertility is a global public health issue – why the dramatic change since 2010? Lifestyles have changed, people are waiting longer to start families – these factors must be playing their part. I wonder if a collective unconscious belief in the power of medicine over the power of nature is growing in prevalence? It's true to say that, as a society, we are over-medicating, more so than ever before in history. With fertility treatments in particular, perhaps we should be asking ourselves, 'Why all the drugs?'

Therapeutic behaviours, actions, treatments or industries almost always begin with the most altruistic of intentions. At some level, the fertility treatment process can feel exclusive, unethical, certainly exploitative of misfortune. It's estimated that a private round of IVF can cost between £3,000 and £5,000 per cycle. (Lindsay J, 2018) According to at least one study, women who conceived with treatment went through an average of 2.7 IVF cycles. (Stewart LM, et al, 2011) What has changed is that people are willing to invest in treatment that wasn't available to previous generations. That pharmaceutical companies are investing millions in fertility-related medication is inevitably changing and shaping the industry itself, as well as our beliefs about the efficacy of medicine compared to nature.

In terms of low success rates, a study found that the odds of success for women of all ages after three IVF cycles were between 34% and 42%. (Stewart LM, et al, 2011) Some clinics quote success rates in terms of live births. Many more in terms of becoming pregnant. This can be highly misleading. A standardised, or regulated practice which addresses how success rates are advertised seems necessary as a minimum. The chances of achieving a pregnancy with IVF hover around one in three. However, some of these women will go on to miscarry, making the chances of actually having a baby closer to one in four. (American Public Media, 2018)

The sad fact is that fertility challenges make you desperate, and this also makes you vulnerable. Many couples who struggle with conception take substantial risks that are not just financial but mental and emotional too. After all, a woman is rarely more vulnerable than when she is a) trying to conceive and b) going through childbirth (especially if medicalised). We hand our bodies over to medical professionals, in the hope that they will make the right decisions, ultimately do their jobs perfectly and make everything work out beautifully for us.

Many see IVF as the answer, as though it's a simple or easy route to take. The somewhat ugly truth is, it *has* become the answer, the market doesn't lie (as we have seen in numbers quoted above). This view does not sufficiently consider the stories of the silent majority – those who walk away baby-less and out of pocket. It's heart-breaking to think about how they have to rebuild and reframe their very lives, whilst they are also far removed from any ongoing care.

To me, there is something unethical about this. My feeling is that fertility treatment shouldn't be a 'baby-making' business at all, but rather a 'family-making' business. In my work in perinatal and postnatal counselling services, it was impossible to ignore how many mothers are affected by the stress of bearing and raising children in our society today, the incidence of postnatal depression and anxiety. We can do better to support mothers who struggle with mental and emotional health challenges. Surely this multibillion-dollar global industry could shoulder their responsibility and offer ongoing support throughout pregnancy and into the first year of a child's life? When we make baby-making the focus, we fail to see the woman, and the mother she will become. We do those women a disservice if we assume a baby makes everything better, as for some women a baby will be a Band-Aid on a gaping wound. We underestimate the lasting effects of 'infertility', the anxiety, the depression, the lives lived in fear, which will not simply disappear with a positive pregnancy test.

Medical intervention into what we term infertility needs to take account of both the short- and the long-term game. A healthier approach would be to focus on the short-term goal of making a pregnancy happen, as well as on a long-term objective of supporting new families to thrive. As a minimum, we need to give more consideration to the context in which a woman/couple experiences 'infertility'.

As an innovation, IVF was ground-breaking. It helps those women and couples who are physically unable to have children to become parents. The rise in numbers of those accessing treatment may well mean that it is being offered to people (like me) who have 'no physical reason' for their 'infertility'; perhaps this is why the success rates aren't higher. While people continue to invest, and money is being made, the process isn't fundamentally likely to change. However, empowerment comes from feeling you have a sense of control – the less control you feel you have, the more you will seek help from external sources, whether or not these present risks to your mental, emotional and financial wellbeing. Empowerment comes from a considered and informed approach to health and enables you to assess what you need and how you are going to get it in positive ways.

Flipping the Script on Infertility

I wonder if it's feasible to become more empowered in our medical treatment, whether we can feel enabled to ask questions and request clarification? I know a full waiting room outside the consultation room must add pressure to both patient and practitioner. It is certainly a downside of western medicine that health professionals are rarely afforded the time to get a full sense of who their patients are, beyond a collection of symptoms and measurements. In general, there is no place for them to ask about, or consider the context of what is going on in a woman's life – what emotional stresses, anxieties or fears she is dealing with – which may impact her fertility health.

If someone had cared to ask and really listened to my response to questions like these, they might well have realised that my struggle was both mental and emotional too. I can look back now and see the blessing in the fact that no one did – another child in my life at that point probably wouldn't have been good for me. In the end, I came to recognise that the 'fix' was in me, not in my reproductive system.

We cannot and should not treat 'infertility' in isolation as if it is the one, single thing wreaking havoc on a woman's life. Everything is connected. When we look at our physical bodies, we must take into account our minds and our emotional, and spiritual, selves.

We need not allow ourselves to be pressured by our advancing age. So many women come to me feeling pressured by their age and this just adds more stress, more anxiety. The pressure of ageing mustn't be a reason to 'go along' with treatments as a default approach. Empowerment is not found in being pressured by the next cycle, our ageing eggs, or the overwhelm of treatment. Empowerment is found in our ability to pause, instead of react. Empowerment is saying, 'I need to take some time to think about this,' doing your own research and coming to informed and considered decisions.

Flipping the Script on Infertility

It's not easy to deviate from the paths ordained to us by authority figures. Those in authority tend to take the role of 'parent'[3] in our lives – telling us what to do and setting the rules and regulations by which we live our lives. Few of us, even as adults, find it easy to say no to our parents. Consultations with medical professionals are similar; we are given our diagnosis, our prognosis, and our treatment options are outlined. We tend not to question authority; we tend to be 'good' children. Just asking the questions we need to ask can give us some of our power back.

My husband and I didn't choose to go down the IVF route; it wasn't for us. I know I would have done anything to have another child, that there wasn't a price I could put on my longing. So, why not try IVF? Because we found we couldn't firmly establish our need for it in our own minds: we had one child, there was no clinical reason found for why we couldn't have another, and the NHS couldn't help us. The price tag was certainly something of a deterrent. I know that if someone had been able to supply us with even one legitimate reason to go ahead, we would have. In the event, it was offered more as a back-handed next step in the absence of the medics knowing what else to suggest. That didn't seem a good enough reason for us. I walked away from the medical route that day and began to explore the holistic therapies I hoped could help us. I never looked back.

I realised that the medical profession couldn't 'fix' my 'infertility'. It was definitely confusing for me that the only so-called cure for

3   'Parent' is an ego-state from the Parent-Adult-Child (PAC) Model, which is a part of Transactional Analysis theory. At any given time, a person experiences and manifests his or her personality through a mixture of behaviours, thoughts, and feelings related to each ego-state.

my gynaecological symptoms was the use of the contraceptive pill. This left us all dumbfounded because treating my symptoms with it would mean that I would never become pregnant. It was in these moments that I saw the humanity of my medical staff; they were unsure of what to fix and how to fix it, just as I was.

The culture in the medical treatment of infertility, the resistance to remove their sterile white coats and their reliance on hiding behind titles and qualifications, lets women down. There were moments during my investigations and treatment that I just wanted to meet another human being who could sit with me, eye-to-eye, in my bewilderment and pain. In those moments, I didn't need clinical answers, all I needed was connection.

Ultimately, there was no pill, no procedure, that could help me. The healing I needed, and eventually found, was not something that could be prescribed, nor bought over the counter.

The most amazing pharmacy can be found in our very own minds. Everything we need can be found within us. Pharmaceutical interventions only mimic what the brain can do to absolute perfection, every chemical we already possess. What gets in the way are our traumas, our conditioning, our beliefs, our very thoughts.

JOURNAL EXERCISE

- Is IVF, or will IVF, play a part in your fertility treatment journey?
- What's going well, and what could help you through the process?
- If you are considering trying the IVF route – what are your feelings about it?
- How could you ensure that you get the best out of your treatment if you decide to go ahead?

If not IVF, what then?

There were so many times I needed to take a break, so many treatments researched and undergone – it was an up, down, back and forth path. I was attempting to make sense of why I was going through it all as I was sure there must be a reason. There are always reasons for everything that happens to us, even if we can't always know what they are at the time.

Acupuncture taught me about the impact of stress on my life – environmentally, emotionally, and nutritionally.

Functional Nutrition taught me that what I needed was someone to consider my whole story, and the importance of feeling heard.

Reflexology taught me about my repressed emotions and gave me a means of letting go.

When I walked away from all of the treatments, I learned that this is how I handle the disappointment I experience when I feel let down, when what they all promised wasn't delivered. Too many times I could see confusion and lack of knowing in the practitioners' eyes. Perhaps my desperately high expectations were only ever destined to lead to disappointment. This is what we humans often do – we expect others to know how to 'fix' our problems or make us happy, and then we become sorely disappointed when they fail to do so to our standards and timescales.

I've learned so much about myself that I would probably never have learned were it not for my 'infertility', for feeling lost in my life. I learned that *everything,* including whether or not I can give my son a sibling, is ultimately about the way I experience the world – the work is only ever within myself. Everything that I was searching for and seeking was inside all along.

'Infertility' is so much more than not being able to get pregnant. 'Infertility' presents us with opportunities to learn and to rediscover who we are at our deepest and most profound level.

T is for trauma...

There are physical traumas to the body that we experience, like a broken limb.

Then there is emotional and psychological trauma which happens in response to deeply distressing or disturbing events. These overwhelm our individual ability to cope, causing feelings of helplessness, and diminishing our sense of self. Such trauma is often the result of an overwhelming amount of stress that exceeds our ability to cope, or to integrate the emotions involved.

It's becoming widely accepted that 'infertility' itself is a trauma. This wasn't so when I first experienced my own struggles. Labels are not always helpful. However, it can be beneficial to be able to put a name to all the emotions and stresses that we go through on our journeys to become mothers. Doing so often normalises our emotional reactions and gives understanding and context to what we experience.

Beyond this, being able to label your difficulties doesn't help you to heal. My hope is that medical professionals are more aware of, and more vigilant in, identifying the signs of the mental health issues which can arise as a result of prolonged uncertainty, fertility treatment, miscarriage, fertility drug side effects and (at times recurrent) loss.

Post-traumatic stress disorder (PTSD) is a condition that may develop following exposure to threatened, or actual, injury or death. Commonly associated with experiences of war, emergency situations or natural disasters, the PTSD is particularly noted for the reliving of traumatic event(s) which are experienced in involuntary flashbacks and nightmares. Other signs can include panic attacks, eating disorders, cognitive delay, and reduced verbal memory capacity. PTSD is most significantly characterised by the fact that it is a response to a single event.

At the time of writing, there are no published studies linking infertility to PTSD, yet anecdotal reports and studies have linked infertility with triggering a stress response associated with PTSD symptoms. While it is possible that a single event arising from an individual's infertility could cause PTSD, identifying infertility as a traumatic stress response to a series of distressing events over a prolonged period of time appears more appropriate. And there we have it.

The conditions that the medical profession collectively term 'infertility' can cause stress and distress.

One study of 488 American women with infertility diagnoses concluded that they felt as anxious or depressed as those diagnosed with cancer, hypertension, or those recovering from a heart attack. (Harvard Health Publishing, 2009) While medical interventions offer much-needed hope, and sometimes alleviate symptoms, studies also suggest that they may add to the stress, anxiety, and grief that patients are already experiencing as a result of infertility itself. The specific type of fertility treatment seems not to be the issue. Rather it is the psychological and emotional process of infertility itself. Over time, PTSD may come to be recognised in context as both the cause, and the potential effect, of long-term infertility.

Flipping the Script on Infertility

The crisis of infertility differs from general traumatic crisis in that there is limited ability to resolve that which is causing stress. As a result, we instead tend to remain in a chronic and prolonged state of crisis. In this respect, the term 'trauma' doesn't have sufficient breadth. Instead, as Allyson Bradow suggests, it could be expanded to include the 'psychological and emotional response to not only physical threats, but also threats to deeply held expectations of life'. (Townsend R, 2019)

Individuals who learn they are considered infertile often experience the completely relatable, but nevertheless distressing, emotions common to those who are grieving any significant loss. Typically, these include shock, grief, depression, anger, and frustration, as well as loss of self-esteem and self-confidence, and a perceived lack of control over one's destiny. The identification of 'loss' in the context of medical infertility is more difficult to address. We tend to have societal rituals to handle loss which arises from death, yet we have nothing which addresses lost dreams of the future and snatched possibilities. Loss, in the context of 'infertility', is hope and despair in equal measure, and experiencing it requires an extensive reorganisation of our constructs of reality or life roadmaps, not least when the outcome is involuntary childlessness.

There isn't enough discussion about how 'infertility' and its treatment can trigger unprocessed past traumas. There is no screening for historical sexual abuse prior to undergoing the invasive procedures involved in diagnosis and treatment. In psychological terms, a woman may (understandably) feel violated in a personal sense by the medical profession, which reduces her to an inventory of symptoms. Some women may feel a sense of invasion from the experience of carrying a baby. Past surgeries or historical emergency medical intervention, whether witnessed or experienced personally, may impact how she engages with treatment at a psychological level. Abortions, miscarriage(s), and recurrent loss must all impact on the treatment process if no counselling has been sought/offered to process these experiences and associated emotions.

Without therapy, we are rarely able to separate ourselves from our experiences.

Screening for mental health challenges could significantly influence our experiences when women look to access fertility treatment. Data from a 2017 study found that fertility treatment providers believe psychological conditions impact pregnancy success rates negatively (75%). Despite this, most providers do not offer formal screening for depression or anxiety (28%) to those seeking fertility treatment. (Hoff HS, Crawford NM, Mersereau JE, 2017)

Mental health screening (and follow-up support) needs to become a routine element of fertility treatment including IVF. Raising awareness and having these discussions brings about the conditions society needs for change to follow.

Without mental health screening and support, fertility providers and the medical profession are failing us and risk exposing us to further trauma, as well as reduced rates of treatment success.

JOURNAL EXERCISE
- Take a little time to reflect on what this section brings to light for you.
- Jot down your feelings or thoughts as they arise.
- If you need support, find a counsellor near you – search https://www.bica.net/find-a-counsellor

Mental health matters...

According to the World Health Organisation (WHO), mental health is 'a state of well-being in which the individual realises his or her own abilities, can cope with the normal stresses of life, can work productively and fruitfully, and is able to make a contribution to his or her community.' (who.int, 2018)

We tend to associate good mental health with positive feelings and healthy functioning, which isn't entirely accurate. Feelings of sadness, anger, ill health or dissatisfaction are all normal parts of our life experience. Many new laws, regulations and approaches arise out of the negative effects of life. Negative feeling states should not be so easily discounted from what 'good' mental health looks like.

No one should feel they have to be positive all of the time. To aim to achieve this would be neither realistic, nor supportive of our mental health. So how can mental health be defined in realistic terms? A more realistic perspective would equate good mental health with a dynamic state of being that resides on an internal equilibrium. It is a state which affects our ability to recognise, regulate and express our emotional states, and to empathise with others. It's also our ability to cope, adjust and adapt flexibly to adverse life events and social functioning. Poor mental health can be identified then when a negative effect is the predominant state of being, one which negatively impacts on our ability to cope with everyday functioning and which is generally triggered (although not always) by adverse life events.

All my physical test results came back 'Normal – no action required'. So it never occurred to me that I'd then be put on courses of fertility drugs and it definitely didn't make much sense to me when I was. Yet I was hopeful, excited even, that this would be successful.

Fertility drugs can have terrible side effects, not least on our mental health. When I was given Clomid, my personal research found that many women experienced awful side effects: did I let it put me off? No. I would have done pretty much anything to get pregnant and I decided that side effects might affect me, but they also might not. One tiny Clomid pill held so much possibility. The possibility of finally becoming pregnant.

Although I didn't experience increased anxiety, I did experience excruciating physical pain. My ovaries felt as though they might burst. A cyst on my right ovary had been deemed no cause for concern even though having sex was incredibly painful. Pain during intercourse was just another aspect of my 'infertility' I'd accepted that I'd have to endure to achieve our objective of becoming pregnant. After my first cycle on Clomid, five large follicles gave us enormous hope for success, the largest measuring 20mm in diameter. My fertility nurse's expression suggested that she expected to find multiple heartbeats at my next appointment. It was incredibly uplifting. My secret hope was that we would have twins. We had always wanted three children. Twins, after all we had been through, would feel like an amazing and wonderful conclusion to our story. My period arrived before I got to that next appointment.

This was my lowest point ever mentally. I wasn't sure if I would or could pick myself back up from this. I sleepwalked through my next cycle on Clomid. By the next cycle, I'd stopped swallowing the pills. I couldn't bear to see those huge follicles, full of promise, and for there then to be no positive outcome. It broke me.

The spiral of depression that followed this treatment was dark and deep. I walked around in a haze where everything looked bleak. Sleepwalking is the closest way of describing how it was to function, work, interact with those around me, despite slow and pervasive disinterest.

Going from the highest of expectations to bitter disappointment was a fall I couldn't recover from. Walking away from treatment wasn't hard, it was like falling off-grid – I just didn't go back. It didn't mean I had given up, though.

Instead I turned to research to help me find other ways to become pregnant. (I now know that stressful life events can trigger obsession). Obsessive thinking is the inability to gain control over recurrent, distressing thoughts and images. The process may be mildly distracting, or it may be utterly absorbing. It may involve developing any repetitive behaviour or action which serves to eliminate the distress around your obsession. In my case, research became a compulsion I developed to help soothe my urge to get pregnant.

Google became my drug of choice as I became addicted to finding the answer to 'The best way to conceive naturally'. There absolutely *had to be* an answer. What I learned was that searching relentlessly for something takes all of your energy. That the uncertainty of my situation was intolerable. That when something is intolerable to us, we find ways to make it bearable.

Constant research made me feel like I could find an answer. It made me feel there was something I could control within the craziness of my infertility diagnosis and treatment. Wherever I was, whether I was at work or at home, whenever an idea popped up or I saw a new approach or study, it would spark an extended online research session, and I would became utterly absorbed. Until, of course, it didn't work. The lure was in the 'What if I stumble across something that will make the difference?' It was a coping mechanism.

At the time I wasn't aware that my research, my sheer obsessiveness, might be a mental health issue. By nature, I'm an overthinker; it's a personality trait, just the way my mind works. As with anything, when a behaviour becomes extreme, when it interferes with our day-to-day lives, it can also affect, or be a symptom of, our mental health.

To my mind, our 'infertility' could certainly be classed as an adverse life event, especially as it is not easily resolved and impacts on our ability to cope and influences multiple areas of our lives. Stress, depression, and anxiety are commonly reported by those who experience fertility issues. Research is now being carried out into the psychological impact of 'infertility' and into prolonged exposure to intrusive fertility treatments on women's moods and wellbeing. (Rooney KL, Domar AD, 2018)

Studies have found that the incidence of depression in 'infertile' couples presenting for fertility treatment is significantly higher (symptoms of 'major depression' from 15%-54%) than for fertile couples. Levels of anxiety are also reported to be significantly higher in couples considered 'infertile' (when compared with the general population), with 8%-28% of infertile couples reporting 'Clinically significant' anxiety. (Prasanta Kumar Deka, Swarnali Sarma, 2010)

A growing number of studies are examining the impact of fertility treatment at different stages of the process, with most focusing on the impact of failed IVF trials. Women presenting for IVF were found to be more depressed, with lower self-esteem and less confidence than a control group of 'fertile' women. Following a failed IVF cycle, the first group of women were then seen to experience a further lowering of self-esteem and increase in depression, relative to their pre-treatment levels. (womensmentalhealth.org, 2018)

This data relates to the women and couples who seek, or are undergoing, treatment. So many more walk away or never pursue it. It's very difficult to identify the full range of experience, and the impact on mental health, across the 'infertility' spectrum. I walked away from treatment because I prioritised my mental health and because, as a couple we did not feel that further treatment was in line with our values. It's safe to assume that there are many, many more women and couples under serious strain related to 'infertility'.

Unresolved mental health issues can lead to self-harm, or even suicide. A 2016 study conducted in association with Middlesex University, London, surveyed over eight hundred women undergoing fertility treatment, and found that, despite the increased availability of IVF and offers of psychological support, emotional distress levels were extremely high. Most of the respondents reported 'Feeling sad, out of control, frustrated, helpless, fearful and worried nearly all of the time.' 90% reported feeling depressed and 42% reported that they experienced suicidal ideation. For those who'd had unsuccessful treatment, reports were of greater distress and more frequent suicidal thoughts. 70% reported detrimental effects to their relationship, and 88% experienced detrimental impact on relationships with family and/ or friends. Only 44% received counselling and of those who did, 75% found it helpful. (Fertility Network UK, 2017)

This highlights that, despite a clear need for counselling, it is difficult to access for many patients, and availability is variable.

However, when patients do access counselling as part of their treatment, the vast majority find it beneficial, as inferred above.

Fertility clinics licensed by the Human Fertilisation and Embryology Authority (HFEA) are required to offer their clients an 'opportunity' to receive counselling about the implications of their treatment before they consent to treatment. However, there is no legal statutory requirement on them, beyond making counselling available, no stipulation about the number of sessions they offer, the fees they charge, nor any minimum standard in terms of its availability: all such features are determined at the discretion of each individual clinic.

As a result, counselling/therapy could be seen by the women and couples seeking treatment as a box-ticking exercise, something they are required to do in order to qualify for treatment, when in fact it should be considered a fundamental and integral part of treatment. There is an opportunity to emphasise the value and benefits of counselling couples and the impact on their treatment outcomes, which is being missed. Currently, counselling focuses on the legal complexities and implications of treatment, rather than the turmoil a woman might go through in response to having to access treatment in the first place.

Fertility treatment providers need also to consider *how* counselling is offered and *how* it can contribute to a woman's care before, during and after treatment. Counselling can play a key role in treatment generally and where treatment is unsuccessful in particular. Leaving the process with empty arms and being left to make sense of your grief unsupported and effectively alone is inhumane.

JOURNAL EXERCISE

- Reflecting on your own experience of mental health, which events have you found difficult to manage?
- Where would you have appreciated more support?
- Have you sought counselling? If yes, did you find it helpful? If no, do you feel it might help you at this point in your life?
- Consider what you would hope to achieve from therapy.

Existential crisis: Who am I and what is the purpose of life?

What is needed is a recognition that fertility *treatment* is not the starting point. By the time we get as far as undergoing investigations or treatment options, women have generally faced months or years of 'trying' and hoping for a successful pregnancy already. Their dreams of what it 'should' be like to start a family have likely been shattered. They may feel as though they've failed before they've even begun, and treatment becomes their only hope of having the family they so desire.

Therapists call this kind of life crisis an 'existential crisis'. It comes with deep and profound impact on the psyche. Rarely will you question your purpose, your very existence, more so than when you're trying to conceive: life itself is inherently in question. 'Who am I if I don't have progeny who will remember that I even existed?' Fundamentally, 'Who/what is my legacy?'

In 1927 Sigmund Freud theorised that there are only two basic drives that serve to motivate all of our thoughts, emotions, and behaviour; sex and aggression. Also known as Eros and Thanatos, or love and death, respectively, he posited that they underlie every motivation we humans experience. These drives encompass our individual survival instincts, and the survival of humanity as a whole to achieve our fundamental purpose, the continuation and protection of our species.

Freud's theories can be complex yet drive theory in its own right gives us an understanding of the motivation of human beings. We are driven by a fear of annihilation and yet, *because of this* we may in fact annihilate ourselves; we see this in war, genocide, the building of walls, the maintaining of borders and collective fear, both cultural and societal, along with the rise in hate and separatism. In times when the internet transcends the very notion of border, state, or nation, we are no longer separated by distance or time, and yet this drive remains.

Fear remains a powerful driving force in our lives and within the collective unconscious.

We see fear in those who try to 'beat' ageing with surgeries or anti-ageing remedies. Death and loss very much remain the biggest taboo in the Western world – our discomfort is profound. Existential crises are ultimately driven by the fear of dying.

A woman who is unable to become pregnant fears that she cannot have children. Yet underlying this fear may lie a fear of death. The death of her hopes and dreams, her lineage and, therefore, herself. Who is she if she doesn't have children? Who are any of us if we leave nothing behind that tells others that we once existed?

We only have to look to TV series 'The Handmaid's Tale', to see how society feels about reproduction. Based on Margaret Atwood's fictional world though it is, it sheds light on a dystopian future where the reproductive rights of women no longer lie within the control of women, following an epidemic of 'infertility'. 'Handmaid' marches have taken place in America, where reproductive/ abortion rights and policies are becoming an increasingly divisive and provocative topic. Abortion rights came under scrutiny in the UK during Brexit, with the Conservative Party's alliance with the DUP[4]. Reproductive rights will always be controversial – they are the ultimate form of control. Control the birth rate and we control the ultimate aim of our species', indeed any species', survival.

Survival in the western world today seems to necessitate producing, consuming, doing more, having more. Society has confused output/production with *worth*. Although capitalism at its finest *may* work for business, it does little for human beings. What we are missing when we equate people with commodities is the potential which lies in our souls, in our spirits, in the miracle of life itself.

When we value output higher than input, a woman who has no children can see herself as worthless. So many women experiencing 'infertility' believe that their partners will leave them, and they carry this burden and shame alone because the perceived duty of women remains, even today, to produce miniature humans due to the very nature of our biology.

This was certainly true for me. I was host to unrealistic and intrusive thoughts that my husband would leave me. He never once suggested that he would, not ever. It's what my inner critic told me because I felt worthless. If I were worthless, why would *anyone* want me, why *would* he want me?

Associating our bodies with production or output means we define our worth in terms of how much we do, how much we create, how busy and/or stressed we are. Busyness is now an

---

4   Democratic Unionist Party (DUP) - a unionist political party in Northern Ireland. The DUP fought to halt an extension of abortion rights to Northern Ireland, forcing thousands of women to travel elsewhere for terminations, or to rely on abortion pills bought online. (Syal R, 2017 theguardian.com)

accepted marker of success and, by association, wealth.

Science, medicine, and society as a whole have lost sight of the miraculous potential of life. We really couldn't treat other humans the way we do, if we hadn't, couldn't start wars or kill our fellow citizens in the street for their skin colour, could we? We couldn't let children starve to death in developing worlds or pass by the homeless man in the street if we considered ourselves walking miracles. If we recognised ourselves as miraculous, the world would look quite different. To cope, to protect ourselves, we diminish the miracles that we are. Instead we consider ourselves merely quantities of flesh, working (or not working) parts, and systems that function well (or not well).

In our collective unconscious, we have lost faith in our own selves. Even though our awareness and knowledge of what to do is innate within our DNA. Even though we aren't accessing faith in ourselves because we're crippled by fear, doubt, worry and uncertainty. We're disempowered by the belief that some authoritative 'other' has the knowledge to fix, determine, and guide our lives that we need. We choose to believe that the answers we seek are outside of us, external. This belief renders us powerless, keeps us in fear, and fear keeps us in perpetual crisis.

We need not fear. The answers we seek lie within us.

JOURNAL EXERCISE

- How do you feel about your own worth as an individual?
- How do you measure your worth?
- What are your feelings about and experience of death?
- What are your feelings about the meaning behind life?

Part Two: Know Thyself

Definition – To know thyself (verb): to get comfortable with who you are, warts and all, the good, the bad, the lovely, and the not-so-lovely.

The ugly, beautiful truth...

On that ordinary day when I heard those seven words, 'Perhaps the problem is in your unconscious', I just sat there in a state of profound confusion. If I were to accept this, it meant my inability to get pregnant was the ultimate in self-sabotage. I couldn't understand it. I couldn't get my head around it. It meant that on a conscious level, I wanted a baby, yet unconsciously, I didn't. As the words rang loudly in my ears and bashed violently around in my head, deep down inside was a distant yet distinct ring of truth.

In the days that followed, I found myself thinking, 'What if it's true?' I had so many reasons to reject these seven words, to refuse to acknowledge even the slightest modicum of truth. I could have walked out of that osteopathy clinic that day and never looked back. I could have become angry with the osteopath, told him exactly what I thought of his preposterous suggestion. I could have spat back at him that he didn't know me, how dare he say such things. I could have... done so many things.

I'm aware that, as a society, we seem to be becoming more and more sensitive to threats to our personal selves: comments on social media are received as personal attacks from faceless trolls who don't know you, have no idea about you and never will. People are quicker to make thoughtless comments, to express their views freely, with seeming lack of consideration for any consequences, either to themselves or the recipient. Whether we are attacked or on the attack, at its root this is a reactive behaviour. When we see or hear a view we are motivated to respond to, we reflect (often publicly) our individual perspective, experience, or mental state. When we receive commentary (often publicly), judgements can hurt, vilify, shame or victim-blame.

It would have been easy to receive those seven little words as victim-blaming. I could have just seen him as insensitive, left him negative feedback and moved on without another thought. I didn't. As much as I didn't *want* it to make sense, if it did then I would have to do something about it, about me – at some level it did make some kind of, albeit uncomfortable, sense.

We are so quick to push back, to react these days. Because contemplating and integrating mean something has to change – an idea, a belief, a principle, and no one likes to be forced into change.

For me, there was (ugly, but in some ways just beautiful) *truth* in what he said to me that day. I didn't know it then; I would come to accept it soon enough.

In the beginning...

Your life begins with who your parents were, with what they believed and experienced. These all went into making you, you. Excavating the foundations of who you are is essential to achieve an understanding of where you've been, where you are and where you want to go.

My own experience of personal therapy has given me an understanding of the who and the what that went before me and shaped the person I've become. There is enormous value in learning how and why to do things differently.

Born in the early eighties to a young black couple in south-east London, I was often described as the loud one who didn't know when to be quiet compared to my older brother. I like to think I'm far more reflective now. I was always the one to object or proffer my opinion though, and that hasn't changed.

My parents divorced when I was four. I've come to learn that more than that there were months/years of inexplicable atmosphere, of negative energy and emotion. It was a hostile environment that affected the whole family. Divorce is just the singular event.

It's important to say here that my parents were open and honest; they never used us children against each other. They got on with it and so did we, we all got on with it amicably and we were all, ostensibly, 'fine'. Sitting in a lecture hall thirty years later, I discovered that four-year-old me couldn't possibly have been fine: four-year-old me would have picked up on this messaging as the accepted way to cope, it undoubtedly set me up for how to 'get on with it' in life.

My parents' divorcing was the right decision; I knew it then and I know it today. Both my parents have remarried and are living happy lives. They are civil to each other and can bear to be in the same room for a few hours. I'm glad that my parents didn't feel they should stay together for us; kids instinctively know when things aren't right. I remember sitting at the top of the stairs listening to my parents argue; taking my money box filled with 2p coins to my mum because I wanted to help her find a way out; I remember waking up one morning to find that she had left, and the relief I felt when she came back that same day after school.

What I don't remember is telling my favourite schoolteacher, Mrs Carter, at the age of four, that my parents were divorcing and that I wanted to live with my mum. I don't remember exactly when my dad moved out. I don't remember my mum crying over our homelessness or the wait in the council offices for emergency accommodation. I don't remember my mum's fear that we might end up in a bedsit, or her relief when we were housed in a two-bedroomed flat on a council estate.

My memories of my childhood are fragmented. I now understand that this is what happens when we experience trauma. It's common when our attachment systems have been interrupted. Dr Gabor Maté says that trauma isn't what happens to us, but what happens *inside* us when we are left to make sense of something that happened *to* us. When our parents are understandably dealing with their own emotions, children are left to deal with their own emotions which they may not understand. We form our own understanding from how our parents cope. If they appear to cope, to be strong, if they hide their hurt and pain, their children may receive the message, loud and clear, that they have to hide theirs too. This became the story of my life. Feelings are not welcome, they are messy, feelings get in the way of 'getting on with it'.

This is a common experience. It's also common to hear it being expressed in throwaway comments:

'Life goes on...'

'No point crying over spilt milk...'

'Suck it up, man up, chin up...'

'Don't wallow...'

'That's life...' (Is it though?)

We all are familiar with some or all of these epithets.

JOURNAL EXERCISE

Reflect on your childhood.

Which of these comments feel familiar to you? What did you hear growing up in your family?

How do you feel these 'throwaway comments' may have affected your reactions to events or your behaviour?

Mama used to say...

Although society is indisputably patriarchal, my experience of family on my mothers' side was very much matriarchal. We spent most of our time as kids in this environment. The women of my family are strong, and at the helm was my grandmother, a tough woman, blind from the age of thirty who raised three daughters and fostered many other children. A member of the Windrush generation, she came to the UK to become a nurse in the NHS. Her stories of her working days were enough to make the young me blush, like how she and her fellow nurses laughed over the patient who was 'hung like a horse'. She was fearsome; it was impossible to ever pull any wool over her eyes even though she couldn't physically see. She missed nothing and would tell you exactly what she thought. She was never one to dwell on a difficult situation or to feel sorry for herself. She set a proud example as the head of our family.

Granny had to be tough, as a black immigrant raising a young family in the fifties and sixties in the UK. My family story is not unique by any means; many more black families came to the shores of Britain looking for a better life for their families. Life was hard. The streets of Britain were not paved with gold. While black immigrants were invited to come to support the country as members of the Commonwealth, they were not welcomed. Instead, they were frequently met with racism, bigotry, and prejudice. Little wonder that if my family had a motto, it would be 'Get on with it'. In the context of the environment my grandparents and parents lived in, that's what they did to survive – get up and get on with it.

My mother has this same conviction, though her demeanour is softer than her mother's. Born in Paddington, London, in 1959, the eldest of three daughters, Jacqui is a strong woman with a big heart. However, she might prefer not to let people see it, it's definitely there. She suffered. I can only imagine what life was like for her, as a divorced black woman under thirty with two children, who found herself and her children homeless. I saw her cry. Twice. I saw her soldier on and sacrifice. I saw her work hard every day and I still do. Her ethics keep her working, keep her getting up, keep her going – for her, there *is* no other choice. Even when her beloved mother, my grandmother, died, she took a single day off work. She and I often debate my generation's work ethic. She bemoans people letting their problems get the better of them. It took time for her to understand why I became a therapist. It made for some interesting discussions about why some people find it difficult to cope.

I very much wanted to be like my mother and my grandmother. For the most part I am, I'm practical, rational, I get up, go to work, struggle through difficult times. My inner voice can be hard and punitive – what a friend calls 'That tough black girl bullshit.' I admire these women who came before me, how could I not? I wouldn't be here if they hadn't struggled on through and survived as they did.

What I've come to understand, though, is that struggling on through doesn't necessarily mean you deal with the things you find difficult. You can struggle on through and carry all that emotional baggage with you. Even as it gets heavier, you just adjust and keep on going. Eventually, you won't be able to ignore the weight of it any longer – it shows up in poor physical health, in unfulfilling relationships, in unsatisfying work, in stress, strain and in your struggle to struggle on through.

JOURNAL EXERCISE
- What were/are the women like in your family?
- What did you learn from them about managing in life?
- What would your family motto be? How do you think this has affected the way you deal with life's difficulties?

Making sense of who we are...

Born in 1954 in St. Lucia, my dad was, and is, what I would call a 'sweet boy', a charming, sweet-talking ladies' man who you can hear coming before you can see him. He's tough, headstrong, knows what he wants, goes after it, and works hard. He's been making his own way in the world ever since he came to the UK at the age of ten, unable to speak English. Self-taught in pretty much everything he does, he's a go-getter who will never sit around waiting for things to happen. He loves his family, his children. We certainly knew when we had done wrong – he was a disciplinarian. He's emotional, perhaps unusually so for a man of his generation, and he wears his heart firmly on his sleeve. He has always been passionate and highly aware of the importance of being involved in racial politics. He used to take my brother, who was older than me, along to participate in equal rights marches and rallies when we were quite young.

When I was eleven, my dad returned to his homeland of St. Lucia, leaving the UK permanently. This was more devastating than the divorce. My dad wasn't the stereotype of the absent black father; he had always been there. At eleven, I was more consciously aware of and able to make more sense of my devastation then four-year-old me. I still never talked about it. Who would I have talked to; my mum? I think she genuinely (and privately) jumped for joy that there would be more distance between them. Could I have talked to my brother? He and my dad had quite a different relationship to mine with him. He may have felt sad, he certainly cried. Yet I also believe that having him at a distance was a relief for my brother too.

For me, it was twenty years before I 'really' talked about it for the first time – with a therapist. Working through repressed feelings of sadness and anger, the feelings that are not easily expressed or even allowed to be expressed as a child took almost a year.

Sifting through those feelings again is tough – I think this is why many of us don't even attempt to do so. It's the hardest work you will ever do, and it's also the most liberating. It's not about blame or shame – it's about being seen and heard in your pain and having your wounded feelings validated. I learned that it was OK to have been angry and hurt that my father left us. That while it does not change the fact of it, that it's totally normal to feel those feelings.

This is just a small part of what I know about my parents' lives. I can only imagine what life was like for them. There is obviously so much more to who they are. They have whole lifetimes of stories and experiences that shaped the people they were and are today. There is more than I can ever possibly know. More that may yet be revealed. These people shaped the person that *I* am, the environment I lived in, the culture I grew up in, the political landscape I moved in.

As babies and children, we have no choice but to adapt to the environment we are born into. Babies are quick to learn how to adapt in order to survive. We are neurobiologically programmed to belong to a group/family. Without our group, we are destined to die. We humans cannot survive alone. Babies cry so that someone picks them up and takes care of them. To survive is our innermost primitive drive. A baby will soon know whether or not their cries result in the attention they need. They adapt to their environment, even when conditions are adverse.

Flipping the Script on Infertility

As humans we adapt, we conform, we compromise, we learn, integrate, follow, push back against or even break the spoken and unspoken rules, procedures, regulations, laws, stipulations and guidelines which exist within our individual family units, groups, cultures, communities, our society. The importance of the model of parenting we experienced on our lives cannot be underestimated. What's even more challenging is to consider the effect we might have on our future children ourselves, whether consciously or unconsciously.

Many object to the concept of blaming/shaming our parents; this confuses being critical of them with not loving them. It's **not** about blame, shame or even criticism. I believe that my parents, in fact all parents, are doing the very best that they can with whatever resources they have; that's about as good as it gets. It's about recognising what your needs were that weren't met, the compromises you made to receive recognition, and how your internal world is built upon the responses and experiences you received from your caregivers as a child. Recognition leads to understanding. Understanding leads to liberation from the maladaptive beliefs and behaviours of your upbringing that no longer serve you in adulthood.

There is not a single person, not even from the most 'ideal' of family backgrounds, who comes through childhood emotionally unscathed. Whatever signifies your childhood for you, what matters is your *perception* of your childhood; it's your experience that counts.

The importance of this is: You cannot give what you didn't have.

Remember this when you think about the childhood your parents or caregivers made for you.

Remember this when you think about being a parent yourself.

It is a generally accepted truth that our parents' generation and their parents' generation tended to parent with lower levels of emotional connection than we see today. There is an inevitability to us now seeing adults who unconsciously act out their childhood hurt, shame, and neglect.

Shamed people shame people, hurt people hurt people.

The more we as parents, future parents, as individuals in the world, are able to acknowledge and deal with our personal baggage, the more aware we become of the conditioning and negative thinking which we have through no fault of our own. Learning to love ourselves first, as any children we may have will need and want us to, the happier and freer both we, and our children, will feel. Any future children we may have, deserve to arrive into and grow in a world which is conducive to their emotional needs.

JOURNAL EXERCISE
- What memories do you have of your childhood?
- What was the environment that you grew up in – culturally, socially, politically?
- Reflect on how your parents/caregivers have shaped the person you are today, what is your internal world like? Do you feel deserving, or needy? Seen and heard or misunderstood and unacknowledged?
- How do you get your needs met? Do you deny them or have unhealthy habits? Are you even aware of what your needs are?
- What do you want for your future children?
- What kind of emotional environment are you creating for your future children to come into?

Mind over matter?

'Give me a child until he is seven, and I will give you the man,' is a Jesuit saying from the 1500s (Ignatius of Loyola, wikiquote.org).

For centuries, man has realised the importance of the influence of a child's caregiver on their development. From the moment we are born, our minds absorb information in order to adapt to and learn from those in their environment.

The nature of the programming we receive comes from our primary relationships, from our parents, their beliefs, their ideas, their prejudices, their motivations, their principles. This is not to say that you will believe what your parents believe, rather that your core beliefs about yourself, others and the world will have been informed by how your caregivers related to you. Unconsciously, their repeated verbal and non-verbal commands, opinions, beliefs, warnings, gestures, and expressions determined their influence on your self-concept, whether positive or negative. Our internal worlds are a reflection of how we experienced those relationships; we become conditioned by our families' ways of relating.

As children we are perceptive observers who note how our parents relate to each other and to others. Children constantly ask the unconscious question, 'How do I get recognition/what I want and need?' Our observation and experience teach us which kinds of behaviour elicit the requisite responses.

Flipping the Script on Infertility

Our conditioning informs whether we experience our world as a safe place, whether we are lovable, whether we are loved. It is how we learn if our emotions are welcome, whether we matter, are important, and wanted. Our conditioning teaches us whether and when it is safe to explore, to have an opinion, to think, to feel, to exist.

The childhood behaviours and beliefs that served us and helped us to survive in our environment growing up can become maladaptive and harmful when they play out, repeatedly and mostly unconsciously, in our adult relationships. Unconsciously we might think, feel, or behave as our parents did, or how they wanted us to behave. We might think, feel, or behave as we did when we were children in our adult relationships.

When we go through difficulties with our fertility, these childhood beliefs and behaviours tend to re-emerge, reaffirming what we think we know and believe about ourselves, the 'I'm no good... I'm a failure... No one understands me... I feel so alone... It's so unfair... Why me?' soundtrack that we may have acquired subconsciously in early life may play on repeat in our minds. This negative voice is the one we tend to subscribe to as children as we make sense of any problems in our environment by reasoning that we ourselves must be the cause of the behaviour of the adults around us.

As adults, these negative beliefs can cause havoc in our lives. When we react to situations, we tend either to be in our 'child'[5]

---

5   'Child' is an ego-state from the Parent-Adult-Child (PAC) Model, which is a part of Transactional Analysis theory.

psychological state or our 'parent[6]' psychological state.

What we *can* do is look closely at our beliefs. What do you catch yourself thinking or saying to others about your experience of 'infertility'? Does it sound more like:

'It's awful, I try, and I try, and I try, and nothing works. I never get what I want. Why do bad things always happen to me?'

Or:

'I'm a good person. I'm trying so hard. Will it all be worth it in the end?'

Our thoughts about life and about how life will be for us play out in our thoughts about our fertility.

They show up in our relationships, our work, and our health – they're always there, continuously repeating and being reinforced. Our minds create our experience and constantly continue to re-create it.

Our programming comes from our unconscious. Change comes from consciousness. To change the course of our lives, we need an understanding of how the mind works.

JOURNAL EXERCISE

- Do you have beliefs that no longer serve you? What can you change them to?
- Are there beliefs about yourself or your world that you have changed since childhood?

---

6   'Parent' is an ego-state from the Parent-Adult-Child (PAC) Model, which is a part of Transactional Analysis theory.

Changing our minds...

The mind can be considered in two respects:
- The 'conscious' (or thinking, analytical) mind.
- The 'unconscious' (or reactive, feeling) mind. This is sometimes also referred to as the 'subconscious mind', meaning 'below awareness'.

The unconscious mind has no ability to accept or reject, doesn't make decisions or decipher information. From birth to around the age of seven, **the unconscious mind is said to be 'wide open'**, meaning it is amenable to suggestion (Murphy J, 1963) to absorbing information from the environment.

As we develop from childhood into adolescence and adulthood, **the conscious mind is used to think**, discern, and analyse information, based on what we have learned in our earlier years. **The conscious mind learns new information.** The *way* in which learning takes place and our attitude to learning are already stored in our unconscious minds.

As adults, our behaviours, thoughts, and feelings seem to be direct responses to stimuli in the here and now. However, our conscious thoughts and feelings may or may not be appropriate to a given situation. Our unconscious responses are useful, in that our responses are automatic, and this frees up our conscious minds from having to analyse or compute every single item of information or trivia. Tying our shoelaces, walking, driving a car are skills that, once learned, are generally not learned again, as our unconscious minds take control and do not require us to think about doing them, rather like the experience of flying on autopilot.

Problems arise when we live in a state of unconscious control, continually reacting to life, according to beliefs about life that were established in childhood and which may not be applicable to our current circumstances.

Happily, our conscious minds are the gatekeepers of our unconscious minds. The more conscious we are of our thoughts, and the more conscious we become of our current states, the more we are able to control what comes through our gates. You have the ability to change your conditioning and, with it, any negative thought patterns. So, why is change so hard?

Habits are hard to break. They are recurrent, often unconscious, patterns of behaviour that are acquired through frequent repetition. It takes twenty-one days of conscious and consistent effort to acquire a new habit. This helps us to change. When it comes to breaking *existing* habits, thoughts, and beliefs, this is more challenging. (duffysrehab.com, 2013)

It takes around ninety days to break an existing habit.

Our brains are like supercomputers and, like any other, computers need to reset themselves. Resetting a brain isn't instantaneous. The fast pace of the society we live in in the west means that it is rare for anything to hold our attention for even nine minutes, let alone ninety days. The mind is resistant to change. Unconsciously, change is perceived as a threat to life. The beliefs and conditions that are established in our childhood years, that formed our self-concept, develop into our systems of survival. Any change will take concerted effort and will – the will to feel and be different.

When we know what we want to change, we *can* make a conscious effort to reset unconscious thoughts and beliefs. We *can* reset our mindset and begin to reject anything that keeps us stuck in turmoil and torment. We *can* reset everything that we think, shift our perspectives and create a new personal reality for ourselves; we *can* basically rewrite our self-concepts and re-model our internal worlds. Doing so can, it must be said, take time and commitment. It is nevertheless possible to reconstruct our inner worlds.

The moment that you realise that the battle is with your own mind is the moment that you can take control of your fertility, of your life.

With daily practice of flexing your mental muscles in this way, what will feel like work initially, soon becomes play. Play may be defined as creation or re-creation; in this context, it can convey a process to be undertaken with kindness, levity, and innovation. In my work as an art therapist working with adults, play is intrinsic to the therapeutic process – we adults forget how to play, we attempt to fix our problems with thinking; solutions do not come from thinking, solutions come from creativity. So, we must learn to play – play with change, play with our thinking, play with re-creating our story from one of misfortune to one of sheroism.

JOURNAL EXERCISE

- How do you think and feel about controlling your own mind?
- Do you think it is possible for you?
- Can you make a commitment to begin to overcome your habitual thinking?

Mum's the word...

I wonder what kind of mother you want/wanted to be. When we are so deeply entrenched in the battle to get pregnant, we may not give much consideration to what motherhood looks like.

I know I didn't, and when our son arrived, nothing could have prepared me for him. I was bitterly disappointed with the version of me that was born into motherhood. I felt like I was treading water and I didn't like it, the feeling of not coping, of being out of control, of having absolutely no idea what to do. This may be a reality of first-time motherhood that no one tends to share.

Pregnancy is the first step on a life journey. As a society, we seem to treat pregnancy as an end in and of itself – its own wonderful event. We herald the pregnant woman and risk dismantling the mother in doing so. We don't pay much attention to the effect of mothering on a child – until we experience shootings in US schools, or teenage knife killings on London streets. Then we wonder where the parents are, we vehemently cast blame on mothers for not knowing where their children are or what they are up to.

You're held through pregnancy with (at least some level of) maternity care, with focused interest and a sense of special privilege. Yet on either side of a pregnancy, it can feel as though you are on your own. Fertility issues can make pregnancy battles seem like trying to reach the peak of Everest, when in reality, you are only at metaphorical base camp, still carrying the burden of stress and risk that you've had to shoulder to reach this point. During pregnancy, birth and in our postnatal lives, every trauma that we've not yet processed is likely to resurface.

If we can afford to invest our time, finances, and energy into conceiving, we should also be investing in the kind of emotional support that will equip us to begin our journey into motherhood. The stylishly dressed bump doesn't matter. The ergonomically designed travel system doesn't matter. What matters is the mother you want to be. Birth is important. Healthy motherhood is key.

Who you are and who you will be for any future children you may have matters.

Our relationship with our mother is the single most impactful relationship we have . It's also, by nature, our first one. We watch her with an intensity beyond our awareness; her every relationship, her every interaction, her coping mechanisms, her habitual patterns – we watch them all and they imprint on our unconscious. This is who you hope to be for someone – their very universe.

I was once told, '**Life comes through you not for you,**' and it had a profound impact on how I thought about my mothering and motherhood. Babies do not come into our lives to fulfil us, they come into the world through us, to experience what it is to live, to discover who they are to become. So, who will you be raising? What kind of person will they be? Because it starts with you. You will be their guide for their lifetime. What role will you play in their lives? How do you want them to experience you? Don't be fooled into thinking that this won't make a difference – the work starts before they are even conceived. If more of us asked ourselves these questions before having children, the world would be a remarkably different place.

JOURNAL EXERCISE

- What investments have you made into your journey to be a mother?
- What changes are you prepared to make to move into motherhood healthy in mind, body, and spirit?
- What stirs in you when you hear that you will become the whole universe for your child?

The mother wound...

Your universe was *your* mother. Your relationship with her, or lack of, has imprinted its learnings on you. You have internalised her in some way, even if this is in an absence of what she was supposed to be or might have been. Looking at her with your 'child' eyes, it's impossible to see the human that she was, with the emotional blocks and wounds that she was carrying or had escaped from.

The term 'mother wound' refers to the unhealed emotional wound/trauma that a mother unintentionally passes down to her child. (Gaba S, 2019) It's a wound inflicted unconsciously when a mother is unable to be there emotionally for her children because she is consumed in her own emotional life. If you weren't raised in an environment of positive emotional health, you cannot give to others what you did not have. So many of us can identify with this experience.

We are all daughters. We all know the spoken and unspoken complexities within our own mother-daughter relationships, however these may manifest. You are a daughter who has a mother, whether or not she is still a part of your life; her influence can never be fully absent. We all have an internalised mother who continues to parent us, both consciously and unconsciously.

This plays out in our lives in approval-seeking, undefined boundaries, self-sacrificing behaviour, difficulty expressing emotions, low self-worth, negative self-talk, social anxiety, and co-dependency. When there is a disconnect from the 'I', from the self – from your wants and needs it becomes difficult to put yourself first, to put your feelings first, to even identify what your needs actually are and even harder to ask for what you need. We relate it to being selfish, and we rate being self-less, when in fact the more connected to the 'I', the self, the more we can relate to others.

JOURNAL EXERCISE

- What do you need to heal and/or let go of when you reflect on your relationship with your mother?
- How can you make peace with your internalised sense of mother, even if this is not your literal mother? How can you be less self-critical? How can you be more self-nurturing?
- If we think of the world, or life itself, as the great mother who cradles us, what sense do you have of her presence in your life?

Mothers are human too...

Not everyone has a difficult relationship with their mother. However, the complexity of mother-daughter relationships may mean that we have difficulty in seeing our mothers as the people they are. Coming to terms with our mother's faults may feel like an unsafe place from which to operate, for both parties. This is a place of great tension and internal conflict, the love for your mother and the criticism you may carry of her mothering may be unbearable, even unthinkable.

For me, for a long time, my biggest fear was my mum dying. I had two very vivid nightmares when I was around six that stayed with me for many years, in which my mother died or sacrificed herself to save me and my brother. I had this unbearable feeling that I couldn't survive if she died. I carried this immense responsibility for my mother. I felt I could not burden her with my feelings and so I also felt like her protector. This was never a conscious decision or a deliberate dynamic in our relationship; it was just how it was for me.

In protecting her, I couldn't burden her with my pain and from my feelings. Eleven-year-old me thought that my mum had enough to deal with and didn't need to handle my feelings too. When we don't know how to manage our feelings, we tell ourselves stories about what others can or can't deal with.

Flipping the Script on Infertility

My mother became extremely important to me – not surprisingly, considering the loss of my father when he emigrated. I am now very aware that my mum could only give from what limited resource she had – she wasn't emotionally available. My mum was in survival mode, literally in fight or flight, and me and my brother were her sidekicks on this journey that we three found ourselves on. She was our world, our means of survival. She was our universe.

Approval never came readily from my mother; she expected a great deal from me because she knew I was capable of delivering. It's just not her way to say, 'Well done!' for small things – that's not how she shows her love, even if at times I needed her to and still do. She's never been through fertility difficulties. There are times when I feel as if she doesn't understand how it must feel to walk in my shoes. I'm also aware that I don't know what it must have felt like for her to feel burdened in her role as a young working mother, carrying the realities of her failed hopes of a promising education, career and marriage with her. Although I don't bear a mother wound *per se*, as with any relationship, I am aware that mine with my mother is fraught with complexity and tensions, between love and struggle, respect and duty, effort and ease. Healing comes from seeing your mother as an individual, a woman in her own right, doing the best she could. When we heal ourselves, we release our mothers of their motherly duty and see her as an equal; we give her the acceptance she was unlikely to have been able to afford herself.

When we heal our mother wounds, whatever their depth, we give our children the gift of a mother who has done her internal work so that they can enter her world far freer of the burden of her emotional baggage than we were.

Flipping the Script on Infertility

When we think of our mothers and about how we ourselves were mothered, we are presented with an opportunity to explore the mother legacy of what has gone before and what is yet to come, you as a mother, your mother as a grandmother, you as a woman, your mother as the woman she is today, not the historical mother you remember through a child's eyes. Doing so will reward you with an understanding of just how vital you are and the impact you can have on the lives of any children you may go on to have.

JOURNAL EXERCISE
- What needs to be left here about your relationship with your mother?
- Let this page absorb any unfinished business, resentment, misunderstanding or lack.
- Leave it here, observe it, release it. No judgement.

The perfect mother...

The archetypal concept of 'mother' as a natural, nurturing, wise and giving goddess has remained fairly fixed in the collective consciousness over time. We tend to receive an image of a woman who is constantly and willingly giving of herself to her world.

We are bombarded with idealised images of 'mother' that are rarely three-dimensional. It is when, or if, we women become mothers ourselves that we discover what being a mother truly means. It is when we become mother figures to those in our life that need guidance, whether that be at work or within our families, or in friendships or roles that we choose to give back and nurture the next generation. It is when we become nurturers to others that we discover what it means to mother and be mothered in accordance with our values and experiences.

Whatever you seek as a woman before having a child tends only to get bigger and feel more vital to your existence afterwards. If you've felt empty, you may feel emptier. If you've felt unfulfilled, you may feel more unfulfilled. If you've felt unworthy, you may feel more unworthy. If you've felt lost, you may feel more lost. Whatever you crave, you will continue to crave, whether or not you choose to accept or deny it, embrace or deflect it.

For me, even though I'm a realist by nature, I still managed to idealise the notion of becoming a mother myself. The reality is, even, or perhaps especially if you view your own mothering through rose-tinted spectacles, life for women doesn't tend to magically change for the better after they've had a baby. If anything, a baby will only highlight what needs to change in her life. I certainly wasn't able to see my baby was a new person in his own right, didn't see that, like any other person coming into my life, a relationship would need to be established with him, and with his thoughts, opinions, personality, and values. At some level, I'd assumed that he would be what I wanted him to be – he was coming *from* me, after all. He'd behave according to my expectations, he'd listen, sit and do what I said, wouldn't he? No. He had his own plans and it came as a shock to me that they definitely weren't part of my agenda at times.

My point in saying this to you is that the fantasy of your own hope for a baby may not be the reality. It's not just the fantasy that you will be happier, it's the fantasy of who this baby will make *you* become. What you hope a baby will give you, that you feel that you can't give or find for yourself right now. Mothering is arduous – it takes everything a woman has, physically, spiritually, and emotionally. We *could* mother from a place of our own habitual unknowing. We *could* raise the children we hope to raise in an environment of our repressed emotion. If we do, our unfinished emotional business *will* inevitably become theirs.

The more that we, as mothers, future mothers, as *women*, grow to understand our feelings, thoughts and beliefs, the more we work on ourselves and discover who we truly are at our core, the more fulfilling our lives will be, whether or not we raise biological children.

In capitalist society, it feels as though we focus disproportionately on a fairy tale of mothering, on the baking of the most ambitious birthday cake for a one-year-old, on co-ordinating outfits with our mini-mes. **Babies become children, who become adolescents, who become adults.** As their mother, you are to be their guide through life; you are their first, and most important, model (not role model) of how to function as a person in the world. Children absorb their mother's beliefs, values, and morals. Mothers generally set the example for how to behave, how to care, how to show empathy and compassion for others, how to value themselves. This makes it our responsibility to consider who and what those babies will become, whether they will achieve what they achieve in spite of, or because of us, to be prepared to take a long, hard look in the mirror and make the changes necessary to make us the women that we want to be.

It takes guts to say we are unhappy, despite all that we have. It takes courage to decide we'll do something about it. We ourselves are the change that is needed. It would be easy to point fingers, make excuses, blame circumstances or others around us. Understanding what it means to be a mother should be key to how we strive to *be* mothers; it's being responsible and accountable for your own life as well as the lives of any children you may have. Life is precious; so *your* life is precious.

My journey to another baby hasn't been how I imagined it to be, nor has it ended. One question defines my journey, however difficult it is to find an answer at times: what kind of person do I want to be? Without asking this of ourselves, we cannot know what kind of mother we want to be.

JOURNAL EXERCISE
- Who do YOU want to be as a person?
- Who do you want to become/be as a mother?

I got a feeling...

The words 'emotions' and 'feelings' are generally used interchangeably to mean basically the same thing. However, we can also think about emotions and feelings as distinct, yet highly related sides of the same coin. On one side of the coin is **emotion: a physiological response to stimuli which is universal, and virtually hard-wired**, such as anger. On the other side of the coin is *your* **feeling: the mental associations and other reactions to the emotion which are highly personal and are acquired through experience** such as frustration, irritation, resentment, or disappointment, which may be expressed passively or assertively. Despite seeming the same, in fact, **emotions precede our feelings**. (Meyer C, 2012)

While emotions are inborn, common to us all, the meanings they acquire and the feelings they prompt are very personal. Because emotions are physical, they can be measured objectively by blood flow, brain activity, facial expression, and body stance. They are more predictable and more easily understood than feelings, which can be tenuous and confusing. There are so many ways to feel an emotion. While **emotions are usually fleeting, the feelings they provoke may persist or grow over a lifetime**.

Our feelings are shaped by individual temperament and experience and can vary enormously from person to person and from situation to situation. Feelings are triggered by emotions, ignited by the thoughts and images that have become associated with an emotion. Because feelings are a mental response, they cannot be measured precisely. However, they can reflect the individual associations we make to particular emotions.

Humans *are* energy.

We are neurobiological creatures, energy in motion, with brains and nervous systems which give function to our physiology. Energy just *is* – it cannot be created or destroyed; it can only be converted from one form to another. This is why we have physical sensations in the body in response to a perceived stimulus, like, for example, butterflies in your stomach in response to a lover's touch. These emotions are a signal to our brains to recognise an input and to feel, respond or react.

Physiologically, the first area of our brains to develop is the brain stem, known as the reptilian brain, which is responsible for primitive functions including sleep, crying, elimination and attachment, as well as instinctive responses communicated via the language of bodily sensation, impulse and touch.

Next to develop is the limbic, or mammalian, brain, which is responsible for sensing danger. It is our emotional and perceptual hub, where you will find the amygdala with our implicit memory (unconscious memory or automatic memory) is found, along with the language of emotion/feeling and sensation.

Last to develop is the prefrontal cortex, or the homo sapiens brain, the rational area of the brain which is responsible for executive functioning, such as reasoning, sense of time, impulse control, planning, memory processing. The prefrontal cortex is responsible for our language of thought and verbal expression.

Understanding the three key areas of brain development gives us an understanding of why thinking, feeling, and behaving is such a complex process. Behaviour and reactions or instincts are stored in the reptilian brain, so we may not always be able to consciously connect to what we felt or thought. Emotions and feelings are located in the mammalian brain, and this may influence how we behave without conscious awareness of the thoughts we may have. The prefrontal cortex holds the language we use to articulate our feelings and bodily sensations in speech.

Sometimes there are no words to sufficiently describe what is felt in our bodies or how we perceive and internalise our experience of others and the world. Perhaps something is always lost in translation. If we can accept that words are not always enough to convey feeling or experience, or that thinking may not adequately compute feeling, then we can learn to follow our innate instinct without rational thought.

We can be *with* our feelings, rather than attempt to think our way *out of* our feelings.

For many of us, our emotions may feel almost alien, like they simply inhabit our bodies and take us over from time to time. We might feel we don't know how to relate to them or what to do with them. When we feel this way, we tend to sweep our feelings under the rug and ignore them. This can sometimes work in the short term. In the longer term, however, repressing our emotions can wreak havoc on our mental, emotional, and physical wellbeing over time.

For thousands of years in ancient China, the Taoists have viewed emotions as information or energy. When something blocks this flow of information within the body, it creates energetic blockage or stagnation. Specific organs relate to certain emotions, for example: fear goes to the kidneys, anger stores in the liver and grief lives in the lungs (Wong C, 2020).

In fact, from a Taoist perspective, many physical illnesses find their root in repressed emotions that cause energetic blockages in the body's meridians. If you've experienced acupuncture for fertility, you may have come across this being referred to as the blocking of the life force or chi.

Many of us learn, subconsciously, to avoid our emotions. We tend instead to pursue distraction and stimulation. We might 'sedate' ourselves with excessive work, food, alcohol, drugs, social media, shopping, 'Netflix & chill', or something else we hope will give us a temporary 'fix'.

Repressing emotions takes tremendous energy.

The cost of not attending to our emotions is higher still. Unhealed wounds mute our experience of positive emotions like joy, wonder, curiosity, enthusiasm, and love. Repressed emotions, left unchecked and unexamined, can damage our relationships, make us miserable, and cause physical disease. When we consider how much time and energy we, as a culture, invest in healing and attempting to optimise the function of our bodies and minds, we can better appreciate how we're mainly working with the effects, rather than the causes of our health issues. If we allow ourselves to consider that the cause of physical disease (*dis-ease*) is mostly emotional, rather than physical, we allow ourselves to consider new approaches to treating health conditions as standard practice. (scottjeffrey.com)

Flipping the Script on Infertility

Some repressed emotions, commonly seen to be the source of much inner tension, inconsistent behaviours, and discontent, may also be emotions which you recognise in how you feel in relation to your own fertility struggles.

Repressed anger and rage

Repressed anger runs through most, if not all, of us. Any form of mistreatment (teasing, bullying, rejection, etc.) or a denial of basic human needs in childhood can lead to repressed rage. The tyrannical part of us can become indignant about virtually anything, fuelling our rage further. Repressed anger may be more 'safely' expressed through sarcasm, teasing, silence or passive aggression. Rage is the acting out of anger – sometimes in our imaginations, our rage might be capable of viciously destroying everything and everyone in its path; repression can therefore feel a safer route. However, repression stops us from accessing the hurt that the anger is obscuring. When we experience 'infertility', we have a right to our anger and hurt, a right to the feeling of being denied one of life's aspirations. It is a maddening reality of what we go through.

Repressed grief and sadness

When we don't fully process loss, we carry it along with us. In repressing our grief, we also suppress authentic joy. If your mind continually returns to images of your past loss (person, place, or thing), it's a sign that you're holding on to something that requires processing or understanding. Crying that doesn't lead to catharsis is usually a form of ego drama[7], not healing. You have a right to be sad about what you're experiencing; you have a right to grieve the loss of what could have been, to recognise it and allow the emotions to flow. We hold our grief and sadness inside us because we think once we open the floodgates it will never stop. It does... and it will.

Repressed shame and guilt

Shame and guilt can be perceived to be the primary operating system of western culture; it can be found in how we parent and teach and also forms the basis of many religions. Shame and guilt are powerful tools of manipulation to get us to do what someone else wants. These emotions are so pervasive in the communication styles of so many of us that we often don't know how to communicate without transmitting these emotions subconsciously. Shame is pervasive and corrosive. It is shaming to admit that we are angry or envious that our sister-in-law or best friend got pregnant without trying, and yet it compounds our shame even further on two levels: 'What is wrong with me that *I* can't get pregnant?' and 'What is wrong with me that I feel these feelings?' The reality is it's only natural to feel this way. The more you can be compassionate with yourself, the more able you will be to realise that all emotions are communications which alert us to what's important to us as individuals.

---

7 'Ego-drama' when we draw our basic energies from our ego and from the highs and lows that our ego undergoes in life, feeling good when things are going well and feeling depressed when they are not. When we are living an ego-drama we are easily, and often, discouraged, angry and depressed. (Rolheiser R, 2010, cath-news.com)

Flipping the Script on Infertility

Repressed hatred

During childhood, many of us are taught that it's not acceptable to hate. Does this make the feeling of hate go away? No. It only forces us to push it into our unconscious. Parents who repress their feelings of hatred communicate this to their children: it's not OK to hate. Children don't experience our words; they absorb our feelings. Even when we say, 'I love you,' these words can be a mask for unowned hatred. Remember, whatever you repress grows stronger in you and gets projected onto others. I hated myself. Deep down, I hated that I wasn't living the life I desired, and that became everyone else's fault. I hated that I couldn't get pregnant. The antidote to hate is compassion – give yourself the compassion you need, the compassion you so freely give to others.

Repressed fear

With normal fear, there's a flight or fight response. Repressed fear, in contrast, immobilises us. Repressed fear makes our world small and limits our perceived options. It also constricts our bodies and damages our kidneys. What are your fears about infertility? That you can't get pregnant? That your partner might leave you? That no one will love you? That you will die alone? That you won't be able to cope with the birth? That you will be a bad mother? That you will be like your mother? That you won't manage, financially or otherwise? Be honest with yourself; what is your deepest fear? Sometimes our deepest fear is that we will be successful, we will get all we desire. Our deepest fear in this context is that we fear we are not good enough to have what we want. Every negative 'What if...?', *can* be reframed with a positive: 'What if I can conceive?',

'What if the birth is easy?', 'What if I am a good mother?', 'What if...?'

Repressed desire

Power, wealth, status, sex, and control dominate our human existence. When we deny the existence of our desires, it makes our repressed envy grow ever stronger. Perhaps your real desire is to travel the world or to start a business or new career. Sometimes we can come so far down a road, it can be difficult to admit when it's not actually quite the right road for us. I was certainly unfulfilled – my desire was to be fulfilled by what I do. Sometimes we think we must know *how* to get what we desire and when we don't know *how*, we repress (and give up on) our desire as we deem it unachievable.

Lean fully into your *what* rather than your *how*.

When your desire is strong enough, the how is not important, you *will* find a way.

Repressed envy

The dominant value in western society is achievement. Comparison and competition drive achievement. The unconscious messages of the achiever's mindset include:

'I'm better than you.'

'Catch me if you can.'

'You'll never be as good as me.'

'I'm a winner.' (implying 'You're a loser.')

The reason that social media can make people depressed is that it reinforces these messages. The hidden message behind many social posts are 'Look how great I am!' and 'Look what I have, and you don't!' This form of subtle competition, if we're not conscious of it, make us envy things we may not even want. Repressed envy leads to depression and anxiety ('I must have it, or else!'). When you are able to reflect on your own envy and to consider what it is that it is trying to bring your attention to, you will see it as your own personal and secret sonar system which guides you to what you want. I was envious of a friend and her beautiful home. When I took the time to reflect, I realised I didn't want *her* house or *her* life, what I wanted was *my own* forever home. When I got in touch with my envy, it told me just what I wanted and just how much I wanted it. That's OK. You can use your repressed feelings to guide you.

JOURNAL EXERCISE
- What feelings do you have that you find it hard to be in touch with?
- What might those feelings be communicating?
- Can you find a way to bring compassion to those feelings?

Trigger (not-so-) happy...

When we talk about 'being triggered', we mean we have what I call 'super-reactions' to certain stimuli. Super-reactions are intense in their impact because we find ourselves defending ourselves from a painful feeling that has been aroused by an experience we are having, rather than responding to the experience itself.
There are two types of trigger – psychological and emotional.

Psychological triggers are related to PTSD. A stimulus, such as a smell, sound, touch, taste or sight, might activate a stress (or 'fight or flight') response in the body, causing us to go into a state of high alert.

When we experience fertility issues, we are *more* likely to confront emotional triggers. A stress response can put us on high alert. We become more and more aware of the pain we are caused by someone's comment or behaviour, or even by our own envy and jealousy.

Can there be anything more triggering than when someone says to you, 'Just don't think about it so much, I'm sure it will happen...'? Or any advice, sought or otherwise, along the lines of, 'Just relax...'. I get it, people feel the need to reassure, or just don't know what else to say, when your pain and uncertainty arouses discomfort in them personally. They feel they must eliminate or relieve their discomfort by 'reassuring' you about something they cannot possibly know for sure. Practising as a therapist continually teaches me that being with another person in their pain means **being with, without fixing**. This takes learning and practice because this isn't something we are taught to do. Know that when someone attempts to reassure you, or doesn't know what to say, it's not about *you* or what you're going through, it's about *them* and their own repressed feelings.

Being considered 'infertile' took me on a tormented journey of being triggered continuously and often unexpectantly. Everywhere I looked were reminders of what I didn't have:

Pregnancy announcements.

Birth announcements (especially if it was a second/third/fourth... child. Especially if their first child was the same age as mine, or worse, younger).

Pregnant women on the train.

'Baby on board' signs in the back of cars.

Women with prams.

Two or more car seats in cars (Why, oh why would I look? I always did – always).

I didn't have to go far for those emotional jolts of pain – it was exhausting. Add to this the fact that avoidance is impossible with Secondary Infertility:

Nursery drop-offs.

School runs.

Play dates.

Birthday parties.

The worst triggers were the comments received when caught off-guard. They come out of nowhere, as if asking about someone's reproductive system isn't personal and/or invasive. The 'You can't have just one!' comment. The 'Having any more?' comment. The 'Only got the one?' comment. The *only* was like salt in a wound, that didn't sting, it burned.

The fact is, when something features in your every thought and feeling, it can't *not* be reflected back to you by the people you encounter and the environments you move in. I know that now.

We can, albeit subconsciously, become conditioned, or addicted to the emotions we feel, and this includes the stress response. Most of our thoughts are habitual. When we feel an emotion, there's a cellular change in the body. Neurotransmitters are released and the physiology of our bodies shift. With this shift, the neural pathways in our brains fire, and then wire in a response. Habitually feeling the same feelings and reacting to them strengthens the neural pathways which will make us seek out the same emotion, albeit subconsciously. This is deemed emotional addiction when the body becomes dependent on its own chemical responses. This changes the reward centre of the brain: even if the emotion makes us miserable, the rush of neurotransmitters is processed as a reward. Emotional addiction is difficult because we're living and breathing our own emotional experience so closely, it is literally beyond the scope of our own awareness.

You may believe your feelings and the way you respond to them is just part of who you are as a person. You may prefer to see how you behave and respond as habit rather than addiction? Feelings can become habitual, a constant state of being. We can become our feelings: we all know someone who seems perpetually angry/sad/bitter/intimidating/moody. This is because their emotional state has become so entrenched it has become a personality trait. We need to consider how, or if, our feelings serve us. If they no longer serve us, what needs to change?

There are many methods and practices to help us to let go of our negative emotions. It is not our goal to *remove* an emotion, because if we're not conscious of the source or trigger of the emotion, it can't be disposed of. Like any method or hack which offers a quick fix, all this does is attempt to trick your mind into believing you've released the emotion, when you've actually just created another way of repressing it. Releasing emotions can quickly become a deceptive form of dissociation where we separate ourselves from them when what we need to do is integrate them.

Becoming conscious and aware of who, or what, triggers you so you manage/limit your exposure is a good place to start. Monitor your reactions to social media and ask yourself who needs to be unfollowed. Whose inputs are more detrimental to your wellbeing than they are beneficial? Give yourself permission to put your feelings first. Self-care isn't all chocolates and bubble baths (although it can be), true self-care is the ability to say no, have difficult conversations, and hold your boundaries with others, all the while practising and noticing what feels good and what doesn't, and acting accordingly. When we go against our feelings, this is when we cause conflict within ourselves. Anxiety, stress, doubt, and resentments all build up, and this leads to repression.

Begin to consider exactly what it was about the comment, behaviour, person or post that bothered you? Was it *what* was said, or *how*? Is the person someone you can trust or someone you keep it casual with? Consider what you really know about the person behind the post – would you swap your life for theirs?

You have the right to be hypersensitive. It is your right to feel whatever it is you feel. Being more discerning about who or what gets to upset you is empowering, though.

Each time we become upset; we give our power away. We are worth more than that.

Flipping the Script on Infertility

There are the people who matter and then there is everyone else. Let's reserve becoming upset for the people and relationships that really matter to us and work on how we can communicate our feelings better, on having our needs met and on feeling seen and heard in our relationships.

There will always be people who think they know what you're going through. There will always be those who make insensitive comments, who don't think before they speak – always. These people are not the problem. When you catch yourself thinking how someone needs to be more considerate, you make *them* responsible for how you feel. If someone or something else is responsible for how you feel, you can never have control over your life. It's our choice.

All we have is choice.

The more I have come to accept my emotions about how I feel about not conceiving, about how I feel about myself, about how I feel about my life, the more I am able to be with myself in my pain, sadness, anger, grief, and envy, the more compassion and forgiveness I am able to feel for myself. The more I turn my focus to what lies within me, the more at peace I feel with what's going on on the outside. It doesn't mean that everything changes. It *does* mean that I am at peace with everything.

This is a daily practice, of committing to feeling how you want to feel, to being who you want to be. Some days you will stumble, we all do. This isn't a reason for us to give up or give in; that's when the practice is most necessary. The brain has neuroplasticity. This means that it can create new pathways based on conscious behaviour at any time during our lives. There is reason to hope, even as it's important to be realistic that changing our thought processes takes a lot of work. The brain favours familiarity: it will inevitably revert to doing what it has always done when you try to change your neural connectivity.

Over time, with conscious awareness, we change.

JOURNAL EXERCISE
- Do you feel any immediate reaction or resistance to a suggestion that you can let go of repressed feelings?
- Are you able to identify some of your unhealthy emotional habits?

Practice
- Tune into the feeling state in your body. What is the feeling state you feel? [For example, anger, sadness, frustration, fear, grief, low mood, worry, shame...]
- Where exactly are you experiencing it in your body? [For example, in the head, throat, chest, gut, feet, hands...]
- How does it feel? [For example, hard, soft, cool, hot, sticky, pulsating, vibrating, heavy...]
- Focus your attention on the physical sensations and the feeling as a whole.
- Allow the feeling and the sensations to be as they are and acknowledge them with your full awareness.
- Relax the tendency to judge or react to the emotion.
- Just be with whatever it is you're feeling. We tend to judge our feelings, by saying things like, 'I shouldn't feel like this.'
- Notice that the emotional energy is arising *within* you,

instead of happening *to* you.

- Breathe deeply from your belly. Take slow, steady, deep breaths, allowing the emotional energy to flow freely through you.
- As you consciously breathe like this, observe how the sensations and your feeling state changes as the emotional energy moves *through* you.
- Keep paying attention to the emotion in a relaxed, centred space.
- After a while, the raw energy of the emotion transmutes or transforms and you may feel it has changed. You may feel something else entirely at this point; gently note what it is. You have worked through and integrated an emotion when you feel at peace once more.

JOURNAL EXERCISE
- Capture anything you noticed during this practice.

To stress or not to stress...

Stress is a contentious issue for those who experience complications with their fertility, not least when it comes to whether or not stress *causes* them. Whether or not it does is something of a moot point. The fact remains that the experience itself is stressful.

Stress is impossible to ignore. It is a common component in our modern-day living. We are all busy, and the demands of a global community means that we don't even have to switch off anymore. The result is that we rarely do.

Stress is a physical and biochemical response to emotional stimuli. It creates a physiological response in us when we are confronted with excessive demands on our coping mechanisms. A stressor is a threat, whether real or perceived, that disturbs our sense of balance or order, or 'homeostasis'. This can occur beyond our conscious aware ness.

Stressors can be seen as the absence of something that the individual perceives as necessary for survival or its threatened loss. When under stress, our adrenal systems are activated and they release the hormones cortisol, adrenaline, and noradrenaline, which affect every organ in our bodies. Stress hormones inhibit the immune system and can result in illness and disease. Instead of being in a state of physiological rest and repair, we instead enter a state of fight, flight, or freeze.

There are three basic forms of stress:

(i) Physical stress, such as accidents, injuries, falls and trauma

(ii) Chemical stress, including bacterial infection, viral infection, foods, alcohol and changes in blood sugar levels

(iii) Emotional stress, such as experiencing tragedy, or loss, work stress and financial pressures.

For humans, the most significant and pervasive stressors are emotional.

In an ideal world, stress hormones would dissipate from our bodies as we discharge the energy they release with physical activities such as running, or by calming the sympathetic nervous system once a perceived threat has passed. However, it seems that threats – whether real or perceived – are omnipresent in our daily lives. Constant states of fear keep us suspended in states of high alert. The sympathetic nervous system responds to feelings of nervousness, apprehension, worry and fear, and its threshold, when set too low, continuously reacts.

When during fertility treatments/*'trying'* to get pregnant are you *not* on high alert?

When are you *not* expecting bad news?

When are you *not* trying to prepare yourself for the worst?

Our 'infertility' battles feel like the fight of our lives. Our sympathetic nervous systems try to defend us from a threat to our continued survival (being prevented from having our own children).

It's the ultimate in double-edged swords. When stress hormone levels are high, you're less likely to conceive, more likely to miscarry. Babies are more likely to be born premature and underweight, meaning that they are more likely to experience developmental delay and metabolic disease later in life. (Dewar G, 2008) Yet enduring 'infertility' is stressful – screening, tests, treatments, appointments, drugs, hormonal changes, surgical procedures, hopes, worries, tears, fears, lows and lower-than-lows. By its very nature, it is a stressful process.

A baby's first environment is its mother. If a woman is in a state of chronic stress and anxiety, then this, ideally, should be addressed and relieved prior to pregnancy. Stress in pregnancy is normal (stress hormones play their part in developing the foetus). However, chronic stress in expectant mothers has adverse effects on delivery and birth as well as on pregnancy. Stress can interrupt the maternal bond a woman forms with her baby and may hard-wire her baby's brain to be anxious and to worry. Emotional stress is prevalent in all of our lives. Many of us are striving to live lives that we think we *should* be living. Happiness has become a thing that we think we can obtain, buy or consume, rather than something which is cultivated, nurtured and chosen; a state which comes as a result of honouring who we are and what we want. Many of us don't really know what we want. We are too scared to allow ourselves to even imagine what we want. This is because for everything we say yes to, there is a no, a death to another option, this belief that there must be a loss – a sacrifice.

In fact, we are taught to sacrifice, to put others first. From a young age, girls in particular tend to be taught to become nurturers and to *give* to everyone but themselves, and boys tend to be taught to be providers and *do* for everyone but themselves. When we sacrifice ourselves for others, we become full of resentment, anger, and even frustration that others aren't grateful for what we do. We then find it difficult to ask for help, because we are taught to put the needs of others before our own. We all tend to have a 'disease to please'. (Winfrey O, 2000)

We can tend to be motivated by this behaviour, even when we pay for it in our stress levels. We all have our own script; you can think of it as your entire life story or as the narratives and stories that we use to communicate our experiences daily. We also have certain default scripts – you notice some people always talk about their ailments or their failures, some people always talk about their bad luck or how worried they are. We all perceive the world in our own way – the world is merely a reflection of our internal reality. Our scripts can be as diverse as we are. Some examples include:

The 'Be strong' script

This script has an inner voice which tells us that no one supports us. Experiencing 'infertility' with this inner soundtrack becomes particularly difficult, because we will unconsciously expect (and confirm, and reconfirm) that no one supports us, no one gets it, there's no one we can talk to. It's isolating and leaves us suffering alone. It's especially detrimental because positive social support is key to the achievement of positive outcomes. (Ozbay F, et al, 2007)

The 'Be perfect' script

What happens to our sense of self if we're unable to fulfil our vision/expectations of our lives? Feeling/being told you are infertile destabilises the very foundations of who you are with the attendant uncertainty and lack of control it brings.

Flipping the Script on Infertility

The 'Try hard' script

Nothing will ever be enough for us when we have this script. Your 'infertility' may become a self-fulfilling prophecy: you must work hard for everything you achieve, including a baby. *Trying* is the operative word here, trying (yet not succeeding), often repeatedly. There is no person in the world trying harder than a woman trying to conceive. Some like to argue she is *trying* too hard. What they can't argue with is the desire, the want, the need.

The 'Please others' script

It could be valuable to explore if our desire to have a baby is located within ourselves? Is it what we really want for ourselves in our quiet moments?

The 'Hurry up' script

If we feel the need to get to our goals faster, to compete with or compare our journey to others, our desperation and urgency to have a baby may be fuelled. We may fill ourselves up with achievement if we succeed. What will be the next goal we feel we must accomplish?

Many, if not all, of these scripts will be familiar to anyone experiencing (in)fertility. I recognise the 'Be strong', 'Hurry up' and 'Try hard' scripts as aspects of my psyche, to varying degrees depending on the situation. I've learned to acknowledge and temper their messages. Once I began to recognise them, I began to see how they influence how I behave, in terms of my fertility and, in fact, in all areas of my life.

- Are you able to identify a script which drives your behaviour?
- What behaviours or stressors are themes for you in your life?

Practice

Awareness is the key. Whatever happens, watch that you don't start to stress *about* your stress.

Practise taking care of yourself. Put yourself first. Put your needs first. It's not selfish; the more we give to ourselves, the more we are able to give to others. We find it so hard to love ourselves, yet we expect our partners and our babies to love us unconditionally. **Find one aspect of yourself that you love.** Reflect on this and the positive effects it has on your life. Meditate on it, or practise feeling gratitude for it. If you find this challenging, *imagine* what it would feel like to like or to love some aspect of yourself and meditate on that feeling. What you focus on expands.

- Capture anything you noticed during this practice.

Practice

Breathe. When we are stressed, we don't breathe. In fact, when you pay attention to your breath, you may realise that you breathe shallowly. When in a stress response, our rate (speed) of breathing increases.

Practise breathing ladders. Always breathe through the nose. Breathe into the lower lobes of the lungs, down deep to where the calming receptors are that prevent panic. When you breathe slowly and rhythmically, you are informing your physiology that you are safe, and your parasympathetic nervous system responds accordingly by inhibiting the body from overworking and restoring the physical systems in our bodies to calm and composed states. **Do more of what you enjoy.** Make time for it. Get intentional about it. If you don't know what you enjoy, think about something that you thought might be interesting but haven't tried, then go and try it. Be open to experiencing.

Find positive support. If you expect that no one understands or can help, then they won't. Expect that you are worthy of having someone to support you in whatever way you need. Talking might not be what you need, it might be someone going along to an appointment with you, or someone running you a bath or making you a cup of tea after a disappointment, or a failed IVF cycle. The gestures don't have to be grand – they do have to be what you need. Don't expect that others will be able to read your mind or just *know;* sometimes you will have to ask. We do love it when people surprise us with their love and compassion after all. In reality, everyone is living their own private lives in their own personal worlds, and every once in a while, it will be important that you **invite them into yours.**

Act or get active. Do something about your stress rather than let it grow and manifest. Exercise. Change your environment. Change your energy – dance. Do a little of whatever makes you feel good. When you focus on your stress, it tends to expand. When you change your perspective, it diminishes. You can change your perspective by changing your environment sometimes, or you can just try to rationalise it away; the choice is yours.

Be flexible. When you have fixed expectations of, and for, the future – uncertainty becomes distressing. It is difficult to feel trust in your life. You trust things, processes, and others, rather than life. **Certainty is a myth.** There is only your belief and your knowing. If we could be certain about how our lives would play out, would they be worth living?

Know your worth. How have you defined yourself? Do you have self-worth? If our self-worth is closely linked to what we do/produce or how we think we are perceived (whether we are accepted or approved of), we risk always being found wanting. However, if your self-worth is located in who you are – just as you are – you will feel more confident in your ability to overcome challenges.

JOURNAL EXERCISE

- Note down your reflections: what will you start doing today to reduce any anxiety or low mood you might be feeling?
- What changes will you make to release your emotional stress?

Being our authentic selves...

In psychotherapy, it is understood that the 'self' in fact consists of many selves, we have plural identities which enable us to function and to operate in the world. We present one persona at work, another at home, another with family, another with friends, another with strangers. This is a healthy way of being: collectively, our identities make up our social identity, our construct of who we think we are as people.

Being 'authentic' has become a buzzword. We often hear that we 'should' be authentic. Despite this, it's rare to hear a definition of what *it* is. In social terms, being 'authentic' has come to mean not filtering our true selves depending on our audience, not wearing a 'mask' to disguise who we are, being exactly who we really are as individuals and being genuine in every decision we make. In essence, it's about being true to yourself. Sometimes this gets confused when people tend to proclaim self-consciously that they are *being* authentic, when they over-share or fail to recognise the difference between connection (authenticity), and exhibitionism.

True authenticity comes from having a personal connection to our inner selves and taking the time we need to mother and nurture ourselves: this is where the road to fulfilment begins. To be authentic with anyone else, we must first come to terms with ourselves.

Flipping the Script on Infertility

For many of us, cultivating a relationship with ourselves can be a daunting proposition because it is so rare that we are encouraged to do so. For some of us, being alone with ourselves can be a frankly terrifying prospect because we may fear boredom and/or the thoughts and memories that may arise.

Feeling lonely is isolating. Whereas being alone can bring peace.

To get to a state of personal contentment, it's necessary to be willing to understand who you are, and what emotions and thoughts you may have. Kindness, compassion, and love for yourself are key to this process. It takes time to build an internal dialogue built on honesty and self-observation, rather than self-deception and avoidance.

There are many ways you can begin to nurture this – and the place to start is with your internal dialogue or self-talk. Considering yourself to be 'infertile' can make your self-talk negative in the extreme, your self-hatred can do more harm than any bully could ever seek to inflict.

The more attention we pay to that voice, the more power we find to change it. What I call 'self-check-ins' are effective ways to foster our positive inner dialogue.

Self-check-ins

Every morning I sit quietly, close my eyes and check in with myself in a silent, internal conversation which tends to cover how I'm feeling, what's going on in my life, what I'm enjoying at the time, what I'm finding challenging. The more I allow myself to get to know myself in this way, the more I'm able to ask myself big questions around purpose and alignment, about who I want to be in my world, about what feels right and what commitments I need to make in order to be true to myself.

Flipping the Script on Infertility

As we begin to become conscious of what we think and feel, we develop an awareness of what lies behind our thoughts and feelings, and can begin to discern why it is we think and feel as we do. We become conscious of our changing feeling states and the thoughts we want to experience more of.

You get to choose *who* you want to be, as well as *how* you want to be.

Journaling

Journaling offers an accessible way to achieve this understanding of ourselves. Writing is a powerful tool which allows us to have distance, to process and integrate our thoughts and feelings. We can empty our minds onto a page and, by reflecting on what's been written, we can begin to understand ourselves more fully.

Connecting with our bodies

The connection we have to our bodies is important. 'Infertility' diagnoses tend not to promote body confidence. It's common to end up in a toxic relationship with our bodies, to despise them for what they are not doing, even though we inhabit them in every other way . We faithfully practise yoga, and consume foods and nutrients that are said to be optimal for bodily health. However, if our thoughts are unhealthy, all our efforts may cancel each other out. The flow of energy in our bodies is directly affected by our thoughts, emotions, our states of health and mind. From incidental stressors and minor ailments to the busy lives we all tend to lead, stress has an effect on our wellbeing. Our emotional, physical, and spiritual health creates a powerful triangle: if you have a physical issue, this creates a weakness in the structure and is revealed in our emotional behaviour.

Meditation

Meditation is highly effective when it comes to moving our levels of awareness from our minds into our bodies. It is particularly valuable when we wish to focus on the heart centre[8]. If meditation is a struggle, you can simply sit and concentrate on the life force you feel within, your breath, your heartbeat, temperature and so on. When you begin to appreciate this life energy within; when you feel into and connect to this energy, you realise that your body is just one element of the many that makes you, you.

Practising gratitude

Practising gratitude is often difficult when we are going through stressful situations or trauma because our focus is firmly fixed on what *isn't* happening, *isn't* working, on *failure*. In fact, this is the most important time to be practising gratitude. Gratitude turns our attention back onto what is good in our lives, onto what we love and appreciate, the little things we're thankful for and make a difference, the things that bring us joy and happiness. No matter what we are going through, life is an amazing experience when we take notice. I spent four years not noticing all of the good that I had in my life because of the *one* thing I didn't.

Practising gratitude is another buzzword concept (like authenticity) for good reason. Gratitude brings us into a state of

8   'Heart Centre' or Chakra - location for the fourth chakra is at the centre of the chest, between the breasts. The Heart chakra is centred on love for oneself and others, on compassion and empathy, on forgiveness and acceptance, on the ability to grieve and reach peace, on transformation and change. The heart chakra can become imbalanced as a result of life experiences that have a strong emotional charge, physical ailments, or significant changes in your environment. (chakras. info)

love, the highest vibration or energy state that we can be in. When we are in this state, good things *will* come to us, because we are aware of all of the good things that *might* happen.

We often hear people say, 'I'm sad about my failed cycle, but I'm grateful for what I have.' It's easy to assume this when we know we should be 'grateful' and often what it is we are recognising is totally rational and cognitive. However, gratitude is a *feeling* state. It's something that is felt rather than thought. This is why it needs to be practised, especially when you are having a difficult time. It's important to identify what works for you, what helps you to focus on and develop gratitude and to find the joy in the now in your daily routine, whether this is meditating on a feeling or jotting down notes every evening. Whatever it is, your mind and body are equally important.

We must take the time we need to build positive relationships with our selves and with our bodies.
We need to invest in the women we are and the women we aspire to be.

JOURNAL EXERCISE

- Do you meditate?
- Do you have, or could you start, a gratitude practice?
- How in tune with your inner self do you feel?

Own your shadow...

In psychotherapy, to 'own your shadow' describes recognising the parts of the self that we are less likely to acknowledge, and even less likely to want to connect with.

The shadow self are the parts of the self we tend to deny, or have difficulty admitting. They are most often the traits that we project onto others because we find them too difficult to own for ourselves. Although such behaviours are often unconscious, with self-awareness we develop the ability to recognise, and begin to own them.

Despite its sinister tone, the term 'shadow self' in fact just refers to our wounded self, the parts of us that have been hurt, the parts whose instinct it is to attack when we are triggered. We see our shadow selves most commonly in behaviours which are driven by envy or jealousy, gossip or hate, passive aggression, resentments or in being judgemental.

When it is difficult to identify another person to attack, we may turn our shadow selves inward with self-sabotaging behaviour and negative self-talk.

With fertility issues, what's rarely discussed is the shadow aspect of desire.

Flipping the Script on Infertility

The desire to have a baby is so deep and so powerful that feelings of envy and jealousy often arise. Whilst we may see these as natural responses, these are the shadow aspects of our desire. It's these emotions we find difficult to own; we tend instead to deny them, repress them, project them onto others or to experience guilt and shame. Our desires' aims are to alter our realities, and these can arise in many ways, including in our wishes, drives, urges, impulses, compulsions, longings, cravings, and yearnings. **A drive is a desire that arises from the body**, for example, the sex drive. **An urge is a desire which has become urgent.** An impulse is a sudden, unconsidered desire which is associated with a particular action. A compulsion is a desire which proves difficult, or impossible, to resist, as we see in obsessive compulsive disorder. Longing is a strong and sustained desire, especially when it is for something which is unattainable or difficult to attain. Craving is an uncomfortable desire. Yearning is a desire accompanied by tenderness or sadness. (Burton N, 2016)

Our yearning desire to have a baby may even feel like a craving. A baby is dearly wanted, yet the feelings this desire causes may be uncomfortable and unwanted. Craving a baby, as with any craving, is linked to emotional desire rather than practical need. There may be no practical need for us to have a baby when we think about *why* it is that we want a baby. When we yearn, we may also covet, and feel our shadow side in jealousy. When we see what we covet as a sign of discontent, and we have self-awareness, jealousy needn't be something which we are ashamed of. We can ask ourselves what it is that we lack, what we are deficient in or what causes us turmoil in its pursuit? Is it really just a baby?

Envy and jealousy stir up all kinds of emotions in us because society teaches us that these feelings make us immoral at some level. However, these emotions are innate reactions to the human condition; we can no more avoid them than we can avoid happiness. It is normal to experience every emotion across the spectrum; it is our job to pay attention to them because they are messengers whose function it is to tell us when something is wrong, when we have erred and when we need to adjust our course in life. Envy can inform us of what it is that we want and what we feel that we lack and nothing more. Once we have understanding, we have no need for fear or shame. Becoming attuned to our emotions helps us to clarify what it is that we want from life. Perhaps it's a baby, perhaps it will become something else. We benefit from understanding our shadow selves because doing so helps us to come to terms with our *whole* selves.

When we deny certain aspects of ourselves, we reject the aspects of our personality which cause us harm.

No one is *all* good or *all* bad.

We each have the capacity for both good and bad. The more we can accept the parts of ourselves that we avoid or repress, the more whole, the more emotionally healthy we will be.

> JOURNAL EXERCISE
> - What part or parts of yourself do you find difficult to own?
> - What comes up for you when you think of your envy or jealousy?
> - Can you find compassion for your shadow aspects of wanting your baby?
> - The more you can own and acknowledge these aspects of yourself, the less they will control you

What's self-love got to do with it?

Do you know *why* you want a baby? Many responses to this question are valid and understandable: 'Because I do!', 'Because I love my partner and that's what comes next,' 'Because I've always wanted a family,' 'Because if not now, then when?', 'Because I'm getting older and time's running out.'

In the early days, I'd have said that it was because we were married and having a baby should come next. It was also what was expected, by our families, our friends, even acquaintances. We went with it. It's like the proverbial chicken and egg – it's hard to be sure which came first, their expectation or yours.

Life can become a bit of a to-do list if we are not careful. We all risk falling into that particular trap. We have expectations of us, and of ourselves that we will get an education, embark on a career, fall in love and perhaps marry, and have kids, preferably in that order. What happens when life doesn't go according to plan? When we hit a bump in the road, and stall, what happens then? We feel failure. We wonder what is next, where we go, what to do?

If we live according to a prescribed road map, we risk losing the passion we have for our own life paths. Not least when we experience challenges with our fertility, we all have a tendency to look longingly over at someone else's life (who may well be looking longingly over at someone else's life), all of us wishing we had what others have. To find happiness, what we need to do is fall back in love with our own lives.

Even though self-love is our first, and arguably most significant love, this isn't something that we are taught or that we tend to teach our children.

It is generally not the experience of young black girls growing up. In the UK at least, our differences from the majority of the population – our hair, our lips, our skin colour – often make us feel undesirable. We black girls grow up receiving messages and pictures of what beauty looks like. I know it never looked like me. When I played at dressing up as a child, I played with a cloth over my hair so I could pretend I had straight European hair just like my dolls.

Girls of all skin colours receive messages and idealised images based on external models of perfectionism growing up that they often, inevitably, then seek to pursue themselves. They are taught to consider very little of what it *means* to be a girl and a woman as a construct, of what it means to be whole as a person.

No wonder self-love is such an alien concept. We know it is something that we *should* have or practise, yet so many of us struggle to even *like* ourselves, let alone love ourselves. Self-love seems implausible, frankly almost laughable. Too many people walk around in lives in which they feel incomplete, broken or in search of a something (or someone) that will make them feel better, less alone.

Lack of love, lack of internal self-love in particular, is corrosive and destructive. We will do anything not to feel that emptiness. When we lack self-love, it is hard to even live in the physical bodies that we call our homes. We dissociate. We numb ourselves. We give no conscious consideration to who we are or to how we are in the world. We pursue external distractions, surround ourselves with *things*, we consume and over-consume.

Very few women have not felt ashamed of their bodies at one time or another. For too many of us, our relationship with our own bodies becomes adversarial from an early age. The lifetime of shame we carry around due to our inability to measure up to culturally defined standards of perfection and beauty weakens our individual sense of self-worth, drains our mental and emotional energy resources, and ultimately undermines our personal and collective power.

For better or worse, our bodies are part of our social identity.

Our body image forms a part of our self-concepts and our identities, the very constructs of who we think we are, how we see ourselves, and how we feel about ourselves. The self is complex and made up of our identity as the overarching construct. This comprises our self-image and body-image, our self-concepts, self-esteem, self-worth, self-efficacy, self-confidence, as well as the nature of our self-talk. All of these inform our internal working models, which in turn form the basis of how we behave and act *in* the world and how we relate *to* the world in our relationships and in our interactions.

It would be very difficult to achieve high self-esteem with a negative body image, it's generally either all negative or all positive. Because the self is fluid and continuously evolving, we are able to change the mental images that we all hold in our minds. It is possible to build our confidence and our self-esteem, to develop our individual sense of worth and to influence the nature of our self-talk. Self-love doesn't seem like such a fanciful notion when we realise that the self isn't a fixed concept.

Flipping the Script on Infertility

False information tends to result in us developing a false self-image. The messages we receive during childhood form what is known as our unconscious conditioning and this influences our self-image. Perhaps you received messages that you're unlovable, that love is conditional, that self-love is egotistical or vain. Perhaps the messages you heard suggested to you that you must look or behave in a certain way in order to receive love.

Our self-images are merely programmes, just like our unconscious thoughts.

There are three elements to a person's self-image:
(i)   the way a person perceives or thinks of themselves
(ii)   the way a person interprets others' perceptions of them or what they think others think
(iii)   the way a person would like to be, their ideal self.
(Ackerman CE, 2020)
At their root, any personal problems tend to lie within our self-image, or its programming. If we take body weight as an example – being overweight is a part of a person's self-image, so when a person goes on a diet without altering their self-image, any weight loss is often temporary because their self-image needs to reflect a slimmer person's thought patterns.

When we experience 'infertility', it's clear to see how having a negative body image will be a self-fulfilling prophecy. If we focus on our *in*fertility – our ageing eggs, our physical malfunction, perhaps our PCOS or endometriosis – we will only experience yet more of the same because that is the image we are creating for ourselves. This is a type of self-sabotage.

As women, there is undoubtedly a detrimental effect on our

body image when we receive an infertility diagnosis. I saw my body as failing me, as broken, as damaged. I constantly focused on what it wasn't doing. I wanted to find a fix for my unknown problem. I hated that my body couldn't do what it was designed to do, what other women were so easily doing.

Correcting our perceptions of our body image is not an easy fix. Healing starts with compassion. Having compassion for ourselves goes a long way to healing the wounds that have been inflicted on us and that we inflict on ourselves. For me, I simply began to refocus on appreciation. I am now able to appreciate my body for the miracle that it is, for the thousands of functions that it performs every second of the day and night that keep me alive, for all that it does that I take for granted, for my limited understanding of how I even breathe.

My body is a miracle and I can appreciate it as such. It is on this that I keep my focus , on what I want (good health) and on what I want as I age (also good health). When I take all else away, I can appreciate how amazing my body is, just as it is. I can also appreciate it for the fact it has given life, and for the potential it has to give life again.

The fact is that we don't even consider *how* our bodies work, until they don't work in the way we expect them to, until we become ill or develop a condition. Until we can't conceive when we want to, in the way that we want to.

Without our physical bodies, we cannot live our lives. We cannot experience the world in which we live – we can't touch, hear, see, taste, or smell. Without our physical bodies, we cannot even perceive the idea of conception.

Self-love starts with showing our bodies some much-needed love. It doesn't matter if you think you're overweight, too tall, too short, too skinny, not pretty enough, not fit enough – put all that aside and just begin to appreciate the fact that you're alive and breathing. Show your body some compassion by starting to change the thoughts you have about your body, the ways you think about your body and, most importantly, the nature of your self-talk.

Negative self-talk is a hidden epidemic which harms so many of us; it's insidious and destructive by nature. Whether it criticises your body, or tells you that you're undeserving or unworthy, that you aren't intelligent enough, what you can or can't do enough of – we *all* have an inner voice inside our minds and it always has an opinion.

I call mine, 'The Critic'. She sits in judgement of everything and everyone, no one is spared her punitive verdict. Her biggest victim was me. Even when I thought I was being nice to myself, 'The Critic' was tough. At times I could see that her voice was necessary, and it still is. It's the voice that makes me get up and get out of self-pity, the one that says, 'Try harder'. It's the voice that gets stuff done. However, it becomes problematic when it slowly chips away at who we are like a silent assassin. When it pushes us too hard, and wants more and more, even when more is beyond our control. We know that struggling to fall pregnant is out of our control, yet that inner critic voice tends to continue to say, 'Try harder', 'Perhaps you're not good enough', 'Perhaps you should have started trying when you were younger', 'Why did we wait so long? We could have had a teenager by now', 'We haven't tried this yet', 'What if we try that...?' It can go on and on.

Self-blame is toxic.

When we combine self-blame with rumination, it reveals our attempt to ease our discomfort by trying to force a solution or to gain an insight into our problems. When faced with ongoing stressors which are beyond our control, this can leave us feeling like the only way to gain control is with overthinking, analysing, research, double-checking, and reassurance-seeking. This is how our minds play tricks on us. Even if, or when, a solution is found, there will always be *another* problem to berate ourselves for.

Our minds also play tricks on us when we tell ourselves that we have no control over this voice or over the thoughts that we think.

You *can* change your inner critic's voice.

You can take back your power. You have within you the power to take back control of who you are and who you want to be. Changing your voice starts with simple awareness. Catch your negativity. Thank your mind for reminding you that it's not nice to think unkind thoughts. Then change the message. Make it believable, don't think things you can't fully imagine yourself being or doing.

Using the words 'I am…[insert X or Y as you see fit]', even if you haven't achieved these things just yet, is powerful. Step fully into liking yourself for who you are and you will find loving yourself will come much more easily.

Like me, you could start by telling yourself things like:

'I'm happy.'

'I'm whole.'

'I'm perfect just as I am.'

'I'm confident.'

I did have to imagine what these would feel like. You can think about the women you admire and about the qualities that they possess that you want to possess. I thought about how I wanted to be like Maya Angelou for her grace and wisdom, and Oprah for her authority and limitless spirit. I thought about how I wanted to channel my inner Michelle Obama with her confidence, elegance, passion, truth-telling and intelligence.

Identify the qualities that matter to you and focus on building these within yourself.

When you find that you're struggling, channel your inner Oprah/ Katniss Everdeen/Wonder Woman/favourite teacher/best friend/ grandmother [Delete, or insert, as appropriate]. Your mind may be the most amazing mechanism in the universe, yet it still cannot tell the difference between what's real and what's imagined. You can channel whatever or whoever it is that helps you to develop the qualities you already have within. Like attracts like. You *have* these qualities; you just don't notice them or pay them enough attention. Instead we tend to doubt, question, second-guess and belittle ourselves.

Changing one aspect of our negative self-images creates a domino effect.

Flipping the Script on Infertility

Other aspects of who we are have to change when we change one aspect of ourselves. There has to be uniformity. This is not to say that negative core beliefs might remain. Work on ourselves is a lifetime practice – there will always be more work you can do, as and when you choose to. There will always be moments where you think you've dealt with something and it comes up again and again. When an issue recurs, you'll already have the tools, and you'll know what to do to handle it quicker. It will no longer destabilise you the way it did when it was beyond your awareness.

JOURNAL EXERCISE
- Who comes to mind when you think about who you admire, or aspire to be like?
- What are their qualities?
- People are mirrors; can you see those same qualities in you? How can you develop them?

Fulfil me up...

Many of those who struggle with their fertility tend to think only in terms of the struggle to get pregnant. There is a belief prevalent in our society that having a baby will deliver fulfilment. A friend once said to me, 'It seems you're only concerned about getting pregnant, not about the part where you have a baby'. That stung. The ugly (beautiful) truth always stings. Although I knew she was right, it was a mirror that I didn't want to look into. Absolutely my thoughts were centred on what *my* body wasn't doing, were on what I wanted my body to do and on finding a fix for *my* body. It was all about me, not a baby. Deep down I knew having a baby at that point wouldn't have been good for me. I had no answers as to what *would* be good for me either. *That* was the problem.

We are all busy searching for meaning in our lives. We all tend to believe that by gaining status or wealth, career success or certain lifestyles, we will somehow achieve fulfilment and will stumble across meaning in the process.

This is a delusion. **The 'I'll be happy when...' delusion.** Seeking something external to us which creates inner fulfilment is a fallacy because external *things* are always transitory, always fleeting – the 'something' [insert new job/new relationship/new home here] never provides happiness which is sustainable. Not even a longed-for baby. As painful as this can be, I know this was my ugly (beautiful) truth.

Flipping the Script on Infertility

Many of us have not been taught about what fulfilment is. We talk a lot about doing, accomplishing, and achieving. This is *supposed* to make us happy. Often, we sacrifice our very happiness to this search for accomplishment and achievement. Nothing outside of ourselves can change what's within us.

Fulfilment is about finding a deep connection to who you are. It's about finding something that you choose because it makes you feel good. It's a practice, a journey which flows, and our inner work lies in the unravelling, in finding out what makes us feel lit up, in what makes us feel light. Fulfilment is knowing and following our true passions. It is surrounding ourselves with the people who make us feel good.

Fulfilment finds you when you have the courage to seek your authentic self.

My husband might've said it was selfish to spend my Saturdays training. He might've taken issue with me when I gave up my job to train full time. He could've said 'You need to get a job now,' when I was out of paid work for two years as I pursued my dream of setting up a private practice. He could have said a lot of things. He didn't say (or even think) any of them.

Friends and family were surprised, found it hard to understand, and made comments about the risk. It wasn't for them to understand. It was for me. It was for me to keep going no matter how hard it got. It was for me to feel the pressure from my husband, from those around me, and to keep on going. I never looked back.

Fulfilment for me was not to be found in motherhood. Motherhood did give me a reason for living, beyond anything else I have experienced. My son is my entire world. His arrival also emphasised that I needed fulfilment, fulfilment which I lacked. It wasn't very apparent to others, or to me, but I projected this need for fulfilment onto him. I would often say that I wanted him to be proud of me. I would imagine him telling his teachers what I did for a living, and I didn't like what I saw in my mind's eye. I imagined him saying 'I don't know what she does, she just works in some job,' and I found this depressing. It scared the hell out of me at the same time.

When I began to own my shadow self, my projection, of course it isn't about my son's judgement, it's about my own. I can see that *I* wasn't proud of me, that working in a random job, or being a stay-at-home mum, wasn't enough for *me*. I wanted more. It scared me because as a married woman, who 'should have' been having children at this particular time in my life, it felt risky to say that what I wanted more was the kind of fulfilment that would come solely from my work. Not my husband's work, career or dreams. Not what we created together. Not my son's work, career, or dreams either. My own work, for me to discover on my own. The prospect of doing things alone can be scary sometimes. Then I felt it like it was almost a betrayal of my marriage vows. Now I know that anything else would have been a betrayal of myself. What of the vows that I had made to myself before we even met? What had happened to them? I'd promised myself I'd always put being happy first in life. I had vowed to myself that I'd always do what I wanted. I'd always wanted, more than anything, to do work that I loved. I had left *my* vows by the wayside and had allowed life to overtake me. I'd ignored my commitment to myself for far, far too long.

If your own desire to have a child is misplaced for whatever reason, it will not go quietly into the night when you become a mother. It will linger and grow, so silently that you may not notice it, so insidiously that you might become adept at ignoring it, yet one day, the emptiness will make you wake up and say to yourself, 'What do I do now?'

- What are the vows you've made to yourself in the past?
- Are you living in line with these vows?
- Which of them (if any) have been forgotten?
- Which do you feel an urge to dust off?

Some of us want to, and try to, have it all. We'll rearrange our lives over and over again in the hope that *this time* will mean we get it all. We drown in confusion and disappointment when we don't. Ask anyone what 'having it all' means to them and they will probably say something like, 'I want to be rich, I want to have a happy family and a job that I enjoy,' or something along these lines. I used to picture (vaguely) what having it all looked like, and it was something similar. All I really knew was that it felt like happiness.

'Having it all' is going to feel and look different to everyone. I know in my bones that 'having it all' is absolutely possible. I also know that the 'all' might not happen at the same time and it definitely won't necessarily be as we expect it to be. Without a clear idea of what fulfilment ('having it all') means to you, you won't ever be able to grasp it; it would be like chasing fairy dust. We tend not to like to imagine what we want clearly, let alone think we can ask for or expect it because we are always in fear of failure. We tell ourselves that we shouldn't get our hopes up. What this does is keep us in lives which at least feel unsatisfying, predictable and safe.

Flipping the Script on Infertility

For me, having it all means feeling deeply fulfilled in myself and in the work that I do. It also means being deeply fulfilled in my role as a mother and a wife within my family. What I've come to realise is that the two are not mutually exclusive, that it's not an either/or choice. Previous generations of women believed that one of these needed to be sacrificed in order to have the other. Consider how happy these women were. Consider how much resentment they carried, how they may have clung on to their sacrifices like a talisman that everyone should be grateful for. Consider the fact that, worse than this, mothers are conditioned to believe that sacrifice goes hand-in-hand with the job. Happiness and motherhood are not happy bedfellows when we look to history. Fulfilment has tended not to rely on motherhood alone.

I am not so deluded as to think that 'having it all' isn't complex. Just because it's complicated, doesn't mean it isn't possible.

Life is compromise, give and take. 'Having it all' takes compromise.

We are all looking for that elusive 'balance', another buzzword of our times. It is worth considering whether life is sustained with 'balance'. Nothing in nature grows when it is out of balance. Balance in the context of fulfilment means making healthy compromises.

Where and when I can grow, I will grow.
Where and when I can let go, I will let go.
Where and when I can accept an idea, I will accept it.
Where and when I can surrender, I will surrender.
Where and when I can commit, I will commit.

Flipping the Script on Infertility

Where and when I can move forward, I will move forward.
Where and when I can take a leap of faith, I will leap.

We are also not taught about what fulfilment is. What is talked about is doing: accomplishing and achieving, and these are supposed to make us happy, when usually these come when we sacrifice our happiness.

The problem is that nothing *outside* of ourselves can change what's *within* us.

Compromise which feels unhealthy is sacrifice. We have been taught to sacrifice who we are in order to be loved.

The truth is you may find the fulfilment you seek in motherhood. You may not. What you need is to be really clear on what it is that you *do* want. It's important that you are able to imagine it vividly, meditate on it, visualise it, journal it. You can spend time finding what it is that you love to do, what lights you up. Even if motherhood is fulfilling for you, mothers, like everyone else, are not one-dimensional creatures, they are many, many things often to many, many people. We can be mothers *and* be whatever else it is that we desire to be too. We can go through our lives without becoming mothers and find fulfilment. When you find what you love to do, it will enhance your life, whether or not you become a mother. It will enable you to model happiness and fulfilment to your children or to the children of those you know and love.

'Procreation is not the only meaning of life, for then life in itself would become meaningless, and something which in itself is meaningless cannot be rendered meaningful merely by its perpetuation.'
Viktor Frankl, Man's Search for Meaning (1959)

You will know fulfilment.

JOURNAL EXERCISE

- What does fulfilment look like for *you*?
- What would it feel like, look like, sound like, taste like? Imagine it vividly, with as many of your senses as you can.
- What step(s) can you take today to move you towards personal fulfilment?

Part Three: Flipping Your Script

Definition – 'To flip' (verb): to make shifts in thoughts, feelings, and/or beliefs.

Let's take one shift, one flip at a time...

Evolution...

We tend to think of life as a straight line, a linear journey from birth to death.

We tend to think that time moves in a single direction, in perpetual forward motion.

We tend to think that healing comes in a straight line from A (wounded) to B (healed).

While these are universal assumptions that many of us have absorbed, life, time, growth, healing and change are in fact all processes which require us to visit and revisit our issues and our lessons learned, our repeated crises and our experiences, milestone moments and flashes of inspiration. Life *is* evolution; we move up, down, forward, backward, and then forward we go again. At times, our learnings turn us upside down and inside out.

Some moments, phases or periods, some challenges, situations or experiences acquire particular prominence over the course of our lives. Some come to define us, to shape who we are.

That which we do not get *over*, we get *through*.

These moments become their own chapters in our lives; they seem to alter the course of our life stories, gaining significance in the timeline of our personal histories. If we let them, they risk altering the course of other lives, whole families, our entire tribes, or communities. These pages in the story of your life that might've broken you (and others) can become your defining moments, moments which inspire rather than do harm.

I thought my infertility diagnosis and treatment would break me. In fact, it was the moment that I heard those seven little 'Perhaps the problem is in your unconscious' words, that became the defining moment of my life.

The thing I had been searching for, the answer to all my fertility prayers, wasn't one I expected. Those words were all that I needed. They woke me up, challenged me to think and feel differently, flipped my reality upside down. I am so incredibly grateful for those words. They began a process of healing in me that saw me seek out living, breathing examples of people who had managed to overcome unbelievable challenges to achieve their dreams. To prove to myself that it was possible to be fulfilled.

Opportunities to grow are often delivered to us in packages we don't like, wrapped in scenarios which may be mentally and emotionally challenging, in phases of life which we fear may destroy the very fabric of our being. By pressing pause, and paying attention to what's inside these opportunities, we can come to realise that life is working *for* us, rather than *against* us, life itself is showing us that change is afoot, that it's time for us to grow, and to evolve.

In the experience of 'infertility', there is an opportunity for profound self-development, for change and growth which can have a positive impact on us, our families, our friends, any children we might have (and in turn, future generations of our families). It is possible to see fertility issues, motherhood, marriage, even the work you choose to do, as layers of transformative self-learning through which you are given the space and the tools with which to grow and become more of who you were always meant to be.

Seeing your 'infertility' as an opportunity is a choice.

Personal, perhaps painful, yes, a choice, nonetheless. Accepting that your 'infertility' may be an opportunity for the greatest project you will ever work on.

***You* are the greatest project you will ever work on.**

JOURNAL EXERCISE
- Perhaps your 'infertility' is in your unconscious?
- What reactions are sparked in you when this question is posed?
- What would you like to change if you could? (You *can*.)

My FMPs – Fertility Mindset Principles...

Philosophers of our time agree that we become what we think about (Nightingale E, 1957). A woman who hopes/tries/aims to conceive inevitably thinks about her fears, worries, and doubts, and about the outcomes that she doesn't want to happen, all the time.

We can allow fear to rule our lives.

Fear is the currency with which we give our power away.

Acceptance is the antithesis of fear.

Acceptance leads to curiosity – curiosity about who we really are as individuals, and what we *really* want.

Curiosity leads to understanding – a new level of awareness of who and what you are and want to become.

Understanding leads to feelings of safety, trust, and love.

In contrast, going through fertility difficulties can make you feel unsafe, uncertain, fearful and isolated.

The first step in embracing your 'infertility' as an opportunity is to feel safe in admitting you're going through it. It means identifying the safe spaces and supportive people with whom you feel able to share that you're not coping. It means finding space to be you, real, imperfect, weighed down by your problems as you may feel. It means feeling safe in admitting to your failures, struggles and stumbles, in making mistakes, to not having all the answers, to not having it all figured out.

Many of us instinctively resist changing ourselves, even when it is our own truths which invite change. We may feel comfortable where we are. It may feel easier to complain, hate, judge others, gossip, or worry, even when it is our very own circumstances we choose to rail against. We risk identifying so closely with what ails and troubles us that it becomes our new norm, our new familiar, part of who we are as people, even when it is to our detriment.

You _can_ find a deeper understanding of yourself, discover your (perhaps buried) desires and act out your personal purpose.

You _can_ fulfil your dreams and have a life which fulfils you, no matter what the outcome of your fertility journey.

Training to become a therapist and mindset coach was nothing short of life-changing for me. While I may not live in a dream mansion with umpteen children round my ankles, _I_ am in charge of my life now. I no longer catch myself spiralling into misery and fear.

The eight principles which follow enabled me to become wholly me. If I could, you can.

The eight Fertility Mindset Principles are:
1. **Accessing awareness**
2. **Regaining responsibility**
3. **Practising presence**
4. **Shifting mindset gears: growth and lack**
5. **Accepting abundance**
6. **Finding focus**
7. **Creating your world with your words**
8. **Repetition is the mother of learning**

Flipping the Script on Infertility

These are the essential principles I adopted to overcome the mental and emotional anguish of my infertility diagnosis and treatment. In fact, you could insert *any* life challenge here. I became aware of these principles over a period of four years. I didn't come across them in the order I've come to realise is helpful (and will allow you to work through them more logically and with greater clarity); they came to me only when I was ready to understand them.

You might choose to work on all eight principles simultaneously. You might focus on one at a time in order to feel you fully and deeply understand how they apply to you in your own life. There is no wrong or right way to approach the principles.

All are powerful ideologies in their own right and they each influence our personal transformation and the mastery we all seek, whether in our fertility journeys or our lives.

Fertility Mindset Principle
1) Accessing awareness

The key to everything is becoming self-aware. Self-awareness is *the* fundamental aspect of my therapy practice. It is essential to my clients' understanding their unconscious beliefs and behaviours. Change, and the power to take fully conscious control of your circumstances, is impossible without awareness.

The term 'awareness' is defined as 'The ability to directly know and to perceive, to feel or be cognizant of events; it can be understood as consciousness itself.' (wikipedia.org)

Many of those who practise mindfulness mistake this for awareness. Mindfulness is defined as 'a quality/state of consciousness, where one focuses one's *awareness* on the present moment.' (lexico.com) Being mindful isn't *being* aware; awareness comes *before* mindfulness. To be mindful, you must first be aware.

In therapeutic terms, psychologist Dr Gary Yontef (1993) describes awareness as 'a form of experience that is loosely defined as being in touch with one's existence.' Essentially to be aware is to be in touch with *what is.* A person who is aware knows what they do, how they do it, what alternatives they may have and the choices that they make. Awareness is the process of knowing that you have control over, choices about, and responsibility for your behaviour and feelings.

Self-awareness gives us choice. This is significant in terms of experiencing 'infertility', and also for our lives in general. Becoming aware of what you feel and why gives you the control you need to make informed decisions about how you *want* to act instead of merely reacting to people, situations, and life events. Whether we continue to have faith in our fertility, or accept our infertility as conclusive, we need to feel in control of our emotions and able to choose positive emotions over negative.

When you achieve greater awareness of your thoughts, you come to realise how greatly they are informed by historical data. Events which prompt us to actively become more self-aware may take place in the here and now, yet the way we think and feel is informed by our past experience.

We may choose *to remember* in the present moment, yet *what is remembered* is often based on past experience.

We are so familiar with how we think about ourselves and the world, we often don't even notice the thoughts we have. It is estimated that we think between fifty thousand and eighty thousand thoughts each and every day. As a minimum, this means we each think an average of over two thousand thoughts every hour. Of these, 80% of our thoughts are negative and 95% are repetitive according to National Science Foundation (2005).

Predominantly and repetitively negative thought patterns reveal how the quality of our inner worlds determines the nature of our very existence. Our health, including the physical, mental and emotional, depends on the tone and content of the messages we express to ourselves, the thoughts we think about ourselves and others, the beliefs we have about the world and our roles within it.

Our realities really are the manifestation of our collective thoughts.

While monitoring the nature of our thoughts is necessary for growth, it's unrealistic to expect us to police more than fifty thousand thoughts each day. What we can do is learn to identify our negative thought processes by raising our awareness of when we experience negative feelings, when we feel 'bad'.

When we feel angry or critical, this arises from a corresponding thought.

It's impossible to think happy thoughts while feeling angry.

It's an entirely natural human response to resist focusing on difficult or wounded feelings. It's often more comfortable to ignore or numb them lest they disrupt our equilibrium and prompt us to find coping mechanisms such as self-harm, in our efforts to *not* feel at all. The more we understand who we are, the more choice we have over the feelings and behaviour we actively want to experience. Self-awareness offers us choices.

Without choice, we repeat the outdated patterns and behaviours which no longer serve us.

Enhancing our personal awareness is as simple as tuning into what is going on for us as individuals, into why we have the feelings and thoughts that we do, into our own unique lived experiences.

Flipping the Script on Infertility

Awareness allows us to become witnesses to our very selves.

When we notice ourselves tuning out, eating to excess, drinking alcohol, distracting ourselves, we are ignoring ourselves, and we tend to self-medicate. Tuning in when we do so allows us to move away from life *happening to us* and towards us *taking control of* what happens to us.

With self-awareness, we can look for patterns in the ways that we explain the world around us, our tendencies to think and perceive what happens to us. It means we stay curious about our feelings and can begin to decipher the messages which lie behind them. Self-awareness enables us to bear witness to our habitual thinking and behaviour, to learn who we are, how we respond in the ways that we do and why.

While self-awareness like this may not come easily, your efforts will be rewarded. The less self-aware you are, the easier it is to respond defensively in your interactions with others. It's very difficult to ask for what you need if you're not clear about what this is. With self-awareness comes improvement in our relationships, healthier states of mind and more positive moods as we come to master the relationship between our thoughts, emotions and behaviours.

The better we become at managing our strong emotional reactions, and the better we know ourselves, the easier it is to express ourselves and our needs and wants clearly to others.

Self-awareness starts from making a commitment to become more self-aware. To begin just notice your personal reactions and responses for the next thirty days.

Practice

Armed with pen or pencil and paper, give yourself twenty minutes to draw a timeline of your life, starting with your birth, and marking all life events you consider significant to your life story, especially those which had considerable impact on you, whether these are major or minor, positive or negative.

JOURNAL EXERCISE

- What do you notice when you review the timeline of your life?
- What gets in the way of you being aware of what you feel and why?
- What can you do to become more aware of your thoughts and reactions, especially those which are negative or that you wish to change?
- Can you identify 'cognitive distortions' (irrationalities) in your thought patterns, any stories you tend to tell yourself which warp the way you think about yourself and others? An example of a cognitive distortion is 'Nobody understands what I'm going through'.
- Is there one particular negative emotion you know that you actively avoid experiencing whenever you can?

Fertility Mindset Principle 2) Regaining responsibility

Reacting, which is so different to responding, can be harmful because our reactions are generally beyond our conscious control. Reactions are pushbacks against a perceived attack on the self. When your self-concept is fragile, you replay past experiences as if they are happening in the present moment. We need to ask ourselves whether what we are reacting to is the person, experience or situation we are facing or whether what we are facing is triggering a subconscious memory of how a person, experience or situation from our past made us feel?

In fact, we do not react to people. We react to our thoughts *about* those people, how we perceive them to be, not as they actually are. We project onto others our perception of who we think they are, what we think they will be, or are thinking, what we assume they will do or say; we do this all the time. We rarely spend time consciously present with purely who or what is in front of us.

We expect people to fully see us and yet we spend little time fully seeing them.

Reacting shuts off our conscious thought processes and blocks the reasoning ('adult'[9]) mind. Reacting shuts down access to our intuitive data about the other person or situation. Reacting stops us from being reflective and aware in the present moment.

When we react to others and blame them for how we feel, the question we must ask ourselves is: 'How does this serve me?' 'How do I grow from this?' 'How do I learn and evolve when I blame or just react to others?'

When our perception is that people are insensitive to our experience when we are going through a life challenge like fertility, how does it serve *us* to think that *they* need to be more sensitive to *us*? How does it serve you to put this onus onto someone else? The question is 'Why do we react so defensively?'

When we can learn to reflect on *why* we are hurting and what we need, we become masters of our lives.

Consider what you are not owning within yourself; what it is that you are unable to give to yourself? When you can love yourself, when you can be kind to yourself, you will no longer focus on the perceived insensitivity and cruelty of others – it will no longer even be in your field of perception.

Practice

Think of a time when someone bothered or upset you and reflect on your reaction.

What was it, in particular, that you found upsetting?

[Note that often what irritates us most about someone else is a quality we dislike in ourselves – people are mirrors.]

---

9   'Adult' is an ego-state from the Parent-Adult-Child (PAC) Model, which is a part of Transactional Analysis theory.

Flipping the Script on Infertility

Capture anything you noticed during this practice.

Regaining responsibility - Radical responsibility and choice

When we become responsible for our own emotions, no one can *make* us feel anything. Our feelings are merely a response to a situation, and in any situation, we have a choice in how we feel about it. It is one of the hardest skills for humans to develop.

Alfred Adler, psychotherapist and founder of Individual Psychology (1912), proposed that all problems are interpersonal problems, meaning that our worries stem from our relationships with others. He suggested we concern ourselves with thoughts and worries about what others might think, say, or do. Adler's concept, the 'separation of tasks', proposed that when we think about our emotional tasks, we need to make the distinction between what's under our control and what's not. His theory reasons that we are often unhappy when we cannot make this distinction and therefore end up worrying about things which shouldn't concern us.

For example, if someone doesn't like you it is not your task to make them like you, your task is to be responsible for your feelings around them not liking you. When you make impositions like, 'S/He should do X...or Y', you are stepping beyond your personal boundaries and into the other person's emotional task. What is always under your control is you – how you feel, how you think and how you act are always under your complete control. If, and how many, children I have is potentially out of my control. However, I have learned that I *can* control how I *think* and *feel* about my fertility struggles.

This is true of any life challenge, or difficult situation. We cannot always control our environments; we cannot stop life events from unfolding in the way they do sometimes.

What *does* lie in your control is how you think and feel about life events.

A lecturer once told me, 'Suffering is trying to control the things we have no control over. There is only what *you* can control, what *others* control, and the rest is up to the universe.' This is a lesson I could listen to on repeat. How much of our lives are spent attempting to bend people, experiences or situations, the words of others, the weather, the climate, the future, to our will? We spend so much of our time trying to control, on trying to get the upper hand, to win, out-do, compete. It's not healthy for us to allow these behaviours/worries/fears to consume us when they are beyond our control. As futile as it is, it seems hard-wired within us to do so. The neuroplasticity of our brains tells us otherwise.

The ability to conceive a baby is out of our control. Yet when, for whatever reason, it is not happening for us, we tend to focus all of our efforts on influencing or trying to improve our ability to conceive, we try to bend it to our will.

I went from despair, to acceptance, to growing as a person and loving my life just as it was/is. That's not to say I don't still have moments where I might think or imagine 'What if...' scenarios – I absolutely do. What I don't do is dwell in depths of despair about what I don't have, the things which are beyond my control.

My task every day has become about being responsible for *my* life. Now my daily practices of gratitude, meditation, affirmations, and reflection are geared toward focusing on how *I* want to live, how *I* want to be in the world, how *I* want to show up for myself. I do whatever it takes to keep me in this positive and self-aware mental and emotional space. I read, I journal, I listen to podcasts, I meditate, I visualise. What I do works for me. It doesn't matter what it is that works for you, what matters is that you do what resonates with you, what keeps you feeling the way you want to feel.

This is a process of unlearning, of letting go, and of refocusing control to centre solely on yourself.

Dr Bruce Lipton, biologist, wrote 'The Biology of Belief'. I had listened to him speaking about his fascinating work on cells and epigenetics many times. It was not until the fifth occasion I'd heard him that I heard something that resonated with me deeply. Sometimes you need to listen or read something many times before you are truly able to understand.

We can *know* something intellectually, yet it is not until we *understand* it that we integrate it into our selves.

On this occasion, Dr Lipton spoke about responsibility, saying that we must take responsibility for our life situations and of how hard we humans find this to achieve. He described a woman with cancer imploring him for an answer on how she could take responsibility for her illness. His response was, 'Once you become aware, you become responsible.' These words hit me like a ton of bricks. Once you become aware, you become responsible for the choices you make.

You become responsible for *how* you choose to respond to what ails you, not for *what* ails you.

I immediately thought about my fertility journey. Later that day, I wrote the following in my journal:

What do I need to take responsibility for?
That I could not get pregnant and more importantly, for the feelings I had surrounding that. It [getting pregnant] gave me something to focus on, to use all my energy on.
What don't I want?
I [no longer] want the feelings of sadness, upset, torment, envy, jealousy, anger over not having another baby.
What do I want?
To feel passion, to feel fulfilled, to feel happiness, joy, love, gratitude for my work, my family, and my life. I want to feel ALIVE. I'm tired of reacting to life, I want to create my life…

I remember writing, 'I want to feel alive,' and feeling shocked to see those words on the page. With shock came the realisation that I had not been living. Moving and breathing, yes. The joy in being alive? Not so much. It made me recognise what a waste of life that was.

How many of us shuffle along through our lives, waiting for something to happen to make them worth living?

The truth is everything worth living for you already have.

Flipping the Script on Infertility

The ugly (beautiful) truth is often that to be able to see it, we must take responsibility for choosing to live our unlived lives.

Regaining responsibility = Response-ability

We so want to say, 'It's not my fault that this happened to me,' (whatever the 'it' is) or 'I've got this issue (X or Y), so that's why I act and feel this way.' We invest so much in believing that this is true.

I took responsibility when I chose to feel sadness when my best friend told me she was pregnant. There were many things I could have felt in that moment. Instead I felt sadness, followed quickly by immense guilt and shame. When we experience difficulties with fertility, we get so used to feeling bad about ourselves that it's easy to begin to look to blame the people, experiences or situations that arouse those feelings. For me, it was looking into cars and seeing two or more car seats and feeling immense pain and sadness that I only had one. It may sound trivial, and like I was torturing myself. In that mental space, it's anything but trivial. It's an enduring torment and yearning for what you don't have.

Our torment is caused by the thoughts we have. In reality, there *is* no torment, instead it is simply the lived expression of your internal world. Your thoughts are the primary cause of everything you feel, and your mind mirrors back to you the sum total of your thoughts all the time. Everything you see, hear, and experience is just an effect, including your feelings.

Flipping the Script on Infertility

As hard as it is to take responsibility for your feelings, the moment that you do is the moment that you are liberated from the dark place of your internal torment and you are able to recognise and accept the possibilities of life.

I think of responsibility as becoming 'response-able'. It is the ability to respond to a person, experience or situation in full awareness of what is happening within you in that moment.

Responsibility affords empowerment and control. So many of us feel controlled by our emotions, and out of control in our life. Powerlessness, uncertainty, and scarcity are such common themes in our society – we see it in ever-increasing consumption, in the erection of walls up to keep 'others' out, in outdated beliefs and votes for divisive policies and increasingly extreme government leaders. Their underlying rhetoric is that 'others' are to be kept out and feared, 'others' are responsible for why our lives are so bad. This rhetoric which leads to hate, division, isolation, and panic.

We can do nothing without first taking responsibility for ourselves and our own actions.

Responsibility means reflecting on how you feel and behave and making a choice about how you want *to continue* to feel and behave.

For me, tuning into my body and feelings helps enormously in this, as does noticing my feelings and how my body responds. Noticing where in your body you feel certain feelings, gives you a pathway to follow in becoming aware of the thoughts you have which then affect your feelings.

Practice

✿ Taking anxiety or worry as an example, I notice that when I become panicky, down or even jealous in response to a person, experience or situation and I begin to pay attention to my thoughts, they often run along the lines of, 'What will they think?' or 'Why wasn't it me?' Just noticing the connection between feelings and thoughts is powerful because feelings are an immediate indicator of negative thoughts – your thoughts and feelings always correspond. Armed with this information, you can then make a choice to stay with your feelings or change them and focus on the positive. This is **LAYER ONE** or the **SURFACE LEVEL** of our self-awareness.

When you start to develop your ability to notice your thoughts and feelings, you can start to reflect. Reflection is important as it shifts your understanding of yourself to a much deeper level. Taking the example of noticing a thought like, 'What will they think?' we might instead ask ourselves, 'Why the self-judgement?' All our thoughts about other people are merely projections of ourselves onto them – as much as we think the problem lies with the other person, it isn't theirs, it's ours to own. When we turn the thought, 'What will they think if I don't have a child?', into 'What will *I* think if I don't have a child?' you bring yourself closer to an understanding of what's important for you . If the corresponding thought is that you must be worthless, you might ask yourself, 'Why do I think I am worthless?' If your answer is 'Because I don't have a child,' then this implies that your sense of worth is solely reliant on any child that you may have, and you might feel able to then ask yourself whether this really is the case. This is **LEVEL TWO** of your awareness, the level of **REFLECTION**. As we come to the next level, we approach the root of our self-awareness.

✿ When we think about the *desire* which is the driving force behind such thoughts of ours, we are able to flip our script.

Desire for a baby + worthiness = the desire to be and feel worthy

It is at this point that your inner work becomes really exciting. Armed with this information about yourself, you are able to ponder on how you can feel worthy *right now*, not a year from now, or after you have borne a child. Right *NOW*. **LAYER THREE** is the layer of **DESIRE**.

When we review the three layers of awareness, it's easy to see that we get to make informed decisions about how we think and feel at the surface level. For me, LAYER THREE (DESIRE) is where we can all strike gold. I believe that all our behaviours start from the highest possible intention, with a desire or wish which yearns to be fulfilled.

The desire for a baby (conscious) versus worthiness (unconscious) is one example of our inner conflict when we experience fertility challenges. Consciously, while I may want a baby, unconsciously it may be worthiness that I seek. In this example, our 'infertility' diagnosis may be a symptom of resistance or a means of self-defence against our internal conflict.

The more energy that we put into our repressions and defences, the less energy we have to function in the world. Our defences are there to protect us against the threat of conflict. The more we can understand why we're conflicted, the more we're able to live our lives to the full.

Many of us choose not to feel, and to remain in denial of what lies at LAYER THREE in our unconscious, or what underlies these feelings. What thrives in the dark generally emerges into the light, either consciously or unconsciously. Fear of who we are at our core may prevent us from examining our thought processes. We fear that it will take a lot of work. We fear that we will have to change or be changed. We fear losing what or who we have.

Responsibility (response-ability) is no trick

Responsibility – a powerful tool which is capable of moving you to a deep understanding of yourself and who you are and want to be in this world. It leads us to empowerment, and to equipping us to take control of our lives by accessing our own thoughts and feelings.

Practice

Identify a thought or emotion and examine it at each of the three layers of your consciousness. In doing so, you are beginning to hone your personal response-ability.

JOURNAL EXERCISE

Capture anything you noticed during this practice.

Fertility Mindset Principle 3) Practising presence

Infertility' has the power to keep you stuck in the past, to keep you thinking about all that's happened to you – the failed cycles, the missed opportunities, the methods you've tried that haven't worked. It's also easy to fall into the trap of continuously projecting ahead into the future, into what you're trying so hard to make happen. When you spend most of your psychological time in the future, you are locating your happiness outside of you, in the distance. It's the proverbial 'When I get to where I'm going, then I'll be happy' story we tell ourselves. It tends not to end happily as you may never get to your chosen destination, it might not be as fulfilling as you'd hope and it might not endure.

Try to take note when you find yourself thinking about the past, or constantly looking ahead to the future in ways which are irrelevant to the very moment you are experiencing at the time. Your future and your past are only invited into your present when you choose to do so. The now is all we will ever have, or experience.

When your thoughts are rooted in the future or the past, you risk missing what's happening in your now. When we pass through the now moments of our lives, our lives can end up passing us by. We do this to ourselves when we are not paying attention.

Flipping the Script on Infertility

When we think about the past, all we are doing is rehearsing what could have been. Rehearsing the past is problematic and destructive: the past *can't* be changed; it's done, set in stone, immutable and immovable.

What we *can* change is our relationship to the past.

Anticipating our future is also problematic, futile even. No matter how much we'd like to convince ourselves otherwise, we can't control exactly how things will go.

It's easy NOT to be present when we are going through fertility treatments. There are doctors' appointments to get to and drugs and supplements to take, cycles to track. There are bills to pay and clothes to clean. There's work to do and reports to write, books to read, family to support and spend time with, and on, and on, and on we go. Add the constant focus on the future, on the next step, and it's no wonder that the present feels so elusive.

Obviously, there are times when it is necessary to look back and remember, or to look ahead and dream. What is important is to be conscious that you are when you are. When it is out of our awareness, we are susceptible to the anxieties that the future may arouse and the guilt that the past may hold.

Practising presence is meditation without meditating.

Practising presence is the stillness which surrounds action, the stillness we learn by actively developing our awareness, noting our breathing, focusing and witnessing with intention.

We come back to our first Fertility Mindset Principle (Accessing awareness). We practise becoming aware of what we are feeling, thinking, or doing in the moment. It's remembering to remember. It's asking, 'Am I aware right now?' of ourselves. The moment that you ask yourself the question, you have awareness.

Practice

Take a breath. Simply draw in a deep breath and then release it gently through your nostrils. When we breathe through our mouth, it triggers a subtle anxiety response, which increases heart rate and redirects blood flow. A slow release of breath through the nose has the opposite effect to mouth-breathing; it evokes a relaxation response. In the Theraveda tradition, the oldest of the Buddhist traditions, meditation practitioners are taught to focus on the out-breath because on the out-breath, nothing happens. Everything falls away for that simple span of time – one breath. (Formica MJ, 2011)

FOCUS: Bring your focus to what are you doing right now. In this present moment, you are reading, you are giving your full attention to the page, the words on the page and their meaning. Multitasking is a fallacy, we cannot give our attention to many things and do them all well, something has to give. It's not possible to read a good book and wash up dishes. When you are present, the focus is on just one thing so, whether you're washing up or making the bed, aim to give your full attention to the task at hand. **WITNESS:** Build your self-awareness by bearing witness to what you are doing, *exactly* what you are doing, in any given moment. Observe how your body moves, observe your thoughts, observe the feelings that are aroused, observe the range and degree of sensations you experience in your body. Become intentional about being present. Become intentional with your focus. Allow yourself to be absorbed in the process of your tasks. This is where stillness and calm lies. The rushing, the stress, and the worry will all fall away. Say to yourself, 'Today I will be present more than not present.' Our thoughts and feelings can only be controlled when we become more aware of our inner world and we allow ourselves to experience the present moment.

Practice

What do you notice when you are intentionally present in the here and now? You might start small like I did. I began by walking, instead of running, up the stairs. Once I'd begun to observe myself, I noticed I rushed everywhere, even when I had plenty of time, so I became intentional about going slower and telling myself I had plenty of time.

Practise small, new ways in which you could be more present in your own life.

JOURNAL EXERCISE
- How would you like to become more present in your daily life?
- What can you change by taking a more intentional approach?

Fertility mindset principle 4) Shifting mindset gears: Growth and lack

I had no idea about mindset.   Before this crisis of infertility, before training as a therapist, before embarking on this journey of transformation I had not even heard of a 'mindset'.   The idea that the thoughts I had were within my control was a concept that was alien to me.   I literally thought that that's how it was, that my feelings were my feelings, that they were not influenced by my thinking. I was a stream of consciousness, a stream of thoughts which were incredibly dark and extremely depressing.   I would think the most awful things about myself, tell myself I was useless, broken, that my 'poor' husband deserved better than to have a useless, broken wife, that I was the worst mother there ever was, that I was being punished for being so.

When we start to learn about our ability to influence our own mindsets, it is like walking out of the fog and discovering new land. I can see that I was broken, that I was miserable and downtrodden and, worst of all, is that I did this to myself.   No one else said those cruel things to me. *I* was thinking and feeling them, me.

How could I possibly bring anything good into my life, when I couldn't see the good in anything I had already? How could I believe I was fertile when all my thoughts were about my 'infertility'? How could I be positive about my chances of becoming pregnant when I was so negative about every aspect of my reality. My mind, my world and my entire reality became a torturous existence while I consumed myself with what *wasn't* happening, with what my body wasn't doing. I know I'm not alone in this. I know that many women going through this have these thoughts, too. I know you may have had these thoughts.

Our answer to this lies in shifting one thought, one shift at a time.

As a concept, this may well sound difficult, perhaps impossible. It's true to say that it can be a challenge at the start. With the intention to make these shifts happen in your self-awareness, thinking differently will soon become a habit. You will not catch all of your unhelpful thoughts, all of the time. Signs and signals from your personal set of circumstances, the way you feel and the people around you will help you to identify the thoughts that benefit from your conscious awareness. In fact, everything and everyone in your life is a reflection of your inner world, whether positive or negative. When we start to tune in to ourselves, we often find that there is no such thing as coincidence, that everything happens for a reason.

Shifting our mindsets starts with the understanding that nothing is absolute. Everyone is in a constant state of growth. Even in this very moment, old cells are dying and new cells are being generated in your body. Life is perpetual. Growth is inevitable.

Who and what you are today, what you think and feel, the image you have of yourself, these are not permanent states. You get to decide who you want to be when you wake up tomorrow. That is exciting.

Shifting mindset gears: Growth mindset

'Growth mindset' centres on the distinction between having a 'fixed' mindset and a 'growth' mindset. It was developed by psychologist Carol Dweck, and popularised in her book, 'Mindset: The New Psychology of Success' (2007). Those with a fixed (or 'lack' or 'infertile') mindset believe that their basic qualities and character traits are fixed, that there is no way they can change or develop them. When they fail, as they inevitably will, it is because they can't, or won't, rationalise their failure. Those with a growth (or 'abundant' or 'fertile') mindset believe that their qualities can be developed through perseverance and hard work.

Growth mindset principles are used widely in performance coaching, education, in business and in goal-setting. The principle is applicable across all areas of life. Success cannot, in fact, be achieved without a growth mindset, even though many of us might be unaware of what such a mindset even looks like. A person's mindset can also arise from their world view or philosophy of life. Our view of life is programmed in childhood (albeit with someone else's programme). Our mindset determines whether our thoughts are for us, or against us.

Being 'infertile' can lead to fixed ways of thinking. It's common to feel that life is against you, that everything is a battle, that people are insensitive or unsupportive, that nothing is working as it should, that there are constant reminders of what you cannot have as though the world is torturing you. When we pursue one hundred and one ways to get pregnant, our mindset has become fixed on the belief that we are the problem, or perhaps that conceiving is difficult to achieve.

Shifting your mindset brings peace of mind. With your new mindset, you are not the problem, others are not the problem, the world is not the problem. With your new mindset, you shift towards creating a world (your inner world) you want to live in. The thoughts you think create your world.

When you adopt a new mindset, seeds are planted which will grow exponentially when attended to with awareness and responsibility. By practising presence, your whole self will become richer, more fertile, and more abundant. Whether you like to think of it as a growth mindset, a fertile mindset or an abundant mindset, adopting one will see you grow, thrive, and become the woman you aspire to be, whether or not you become a mother.

Shifting is simple, as simple as flipping your script.
We shift by turning our habitual thoughts, narratives, stories,
our scripts, on their heads.
We shift ourselves from lack to growth, from negative to
positive.

Flipping the Script on Infertility

JOURNAL EXERCISE

- Can you continue to live in your own private world of turmoil and anguish?
- Are you living the way you want to live?
- What kind of life do you want to create for yourself?

Shifting mindset gears:
Lack mindset

I was originally introduced to this approach to mindset when I started my private practice. The timing was perfect – I had so much to learn about being successful, managing my anxieties and my overwhelm, and the way I thought about my role in the world. There were so many books, videos, podcasts on mindset theory to consume, so many perspectives which might influence and change the way I thought.

After a while, I came to realise that my mindset was a 'lack mindset'. I can't help wondering why this concept is most often related to becoming successful or achieving goals, usually career or money goals, when thinking this way affected *every* area of my life. With a lack mindset, achieving any goal or dream was an uphill battle.

Those with lack mindset live in a fear-based world of never having enough – enough money, time, connections, attention, rest, health, happiness, credentials, power, or love. Living with a perspective of lack prevents our ability to take risks and cuts off any expectation we might have of receiving happiness or finding joy in life itself. Lack is defined as 'a state of being without, or not having enough of something' (lexico.com).

Flipping the Script on Infertility

When I reflected on my personal journey in general and my struggle to conceive in particular, I could see a lack mindset domino effect was influencing every aspect of my life. To have a lack mentality is to feel you are in deficit. I was soul-suckingly stuck in my (perception of) lack at the time, in deficit to the max; I was suffering.

Having a lack mindset means your perception of being without slowly pervades every corner of your life. Lack is like a smokescreen through which the good in your life always seems fleeting, you can't grasp hold of it for long enough. At its worst, you're unable to see or appreciate the good things you have.

You might have a 'good' job and make 'good' money. You might still feel lacking. The lack mindset, from wherever it originates, becomes so consuming that it can taint what 'should' bring you satisfaction, like said 'good' job. So many of us live lives that so many others aspire to. We appear to have it all: money, family, friends, perhaps fame, perhaps looks. Yet some of these people who appear to have it all choose to end their lives regardless; they choose to take their own lives. This is deficit at its most dangerous.

The lack mindset or deficit will be caused by something different for everyone, similarly with the antidote for it. What lack mindset does is become a giant black hole capable of consuming everything in its path. It can even feel like it might consume you.

I became a mother and lost me – **I was lacking in a social identity.** I was working in a job that I loathed – **I was deeply lacking in fulfilment.**
I was out of pocket, paying for childcare – **I was lacking financially.** I was trying for another baby and failing – **I was lacking in wholeness.**

Altogether, this did not make for a happy picture.

Horrible job + paying for someone else to take care of my child + financial deficit = resentment (by the shedload).

Even at home, my resentment tended to colour our family life. Resentment and discontent tend to spread and they are toxic. My marriage is a happy one and so is my home. Despite this, I was deeply unhappy during this period. As is natural in family units, if I wasn't happy, no one else could be happy either.

The truth is, no one can *make* you happy, not even a child. Happiness is an inside job – you can't pursue it, buy it, or grab hold of it; it's a state of being. The sooner we come to realise that as individuals we are responsible for our own happiness, the better our relationships can become; we will stop expecting to find it in others and in things. We stop requiring it of others and will no longer be disappointed if they don't deliver what we need; we will stop burdening those we love and want to love.

Only you know what can make you happy. I can tell you that happiness does not reside in lack. Happiness is by far one of the most valuable assets in life, despite the fact that it doesn't cost a thing. It simply isn't true that happiness is something we can pursue, purchase or be given.

Happiness is found in being fully present in your life, in being authentically who you are – all of who you are, not just the good bits. Happiness is chosen. Happiness is about choosing happiness. Choosing gratitude. Choosing love. Choosing life.

Any trauma that comes from 'infertility' (or that which arises from trying to conceive) comes from placing our happiness *outside* of ourselves.

Flipping the Script on Infertility

JOURNAL EXERCISE

- Do you believe that any future children you may have would want you to be unhappy?
- Would they want to come into a world in which their mother is unhappy?
- How would it feel to be born to a mother who relies on them for her happiness?

Shifting mindset gears:
When lack begets lack

When you are in a psychological state of lack, you will only find, and attract, more lack.

When I decided to try for Baby Number Two – I was lacking in being able to become pregnant. There was no explanation.

I went deeper into the black hole of deficit and I began to drown in it.

Who was I? I was absent meaning. I was absent fulfilment. I know now that if you increase the meaning in your life, you decrease the despair. Despair is just suffering without meaning.

Everyone's lack, or deficit, will look and feel different. Everyone's suffering will be different. Everyone's idea of meaning will be different. For some, it will be a lack of money or of power, for others a lack of security or safety, for others still, it will be a lack of love. The ripple effects of whatever you lack will be felt in every area of your life.

I was lacking fulfilment. Somehow, the idea that Baby Number Two was the solution became logical, even when it wasn't sensible. Logical because the timing was right – my son was two years old. Logical because it's not advisable to start a new career and go on maternity leave shortly after. Was it sensible? No. Mentally and emotionally, I wasn't in a good place at all.

Deciding to try for Baby Number Two was motivated by avoidance – the avoidance of the pain of an unfulfilled life. It's not that growing my family wasn't (isn't) a goal, it's that it wasn't the right goal for me that would deliver what I needed *at that time*. I had the misguided perception that my choice was between **either** my family **or** my career, rather than aiming to achieve **both** a career **and** be able to grow my family. Lack mindsets have a tendency to make us think we **can't**. That is a story we often see and hear perpetuated in society – when asked, most people will tell you, 'You can't have it all.'

When your behaviour is motivated by avoidance to move *away from* pain or is directed by what you *don't* want and/or the threat of negative consequences, your focus is on the negative outcome: this is stressful. It means you are driven by fear and anxiety which keeps you motivated to remain fixated on your negative thoughts and feelings.

When experiencing fertility issues, we tend to find that we women fixate on what's *not* working, on time running out, on expecting treatment not to work, on 'knowing' that conception hasn't happened, on the perceived unfairness of our situation, on how awful and despairing our situation is. Many of us express that we feel 'broken' or 'empty'. I felt it too. Feeling 'broken' and 'empty' are '**away from**' motivators, strategies to avoid the pain of feeling empty. The antithesis of the pain is to feel 'full'; feeling psychologically and physically 'full' may equate to a full or pregnant belly. We long to be filled, and we humans tend to look to external sources to do this for us. A foetus may fill a woman for nine months, yet it is important to remember that a baby is, and will ultimately be, external from her. If we are expecting to be 'filled' by our children, both they and we will be found wanting.

Lack tends to generate lack. Focusing on being broken or empty, or fixating on what's not happening, will only bring you more brokenness, more emptiness, more of what's not happening. A lack mentality sabotages. How you think and what you believe about life determines the choices you make and ultimately governs how you behave with others as well as being reflected in your attitude and approach to yourself.

I remember looking at pregnant women and feeling envy or jealousy, immediately followed by guilt and shame. I felt the same whenever I saw those 'Baby on board' signs in cars. The same whenever an acquaintance announced a pregnancy on social media. The same whenever I saw a young family with a baby. Envy, jealousy, guilt and shame. With these feelings quickly came despairing thoughts like 'Why not me?' or self-loathing thoughts like 'What's wrong with me?', 'Why am *I* broken?', or 'It's not fair!'

Whenever you look at someone else and feel inferior, or less than, whenever you feel that they have something that *you* want, you are feeling a lack from their success or your perception of their success. Whenever you compare yourself to someone else and find yourself lacking, you only reinforce and remain in a state of lack. Sadly, lack begets lack.

We can identify our lack mindset when we catch ourselves concentrating our focus on what's not happening for us, on the difficulties and challenges, on our worries and fears, on the bad things in life and our expectations that things will get worse for us. Many of us have been conditioned to be this way. Many of us have been raised to view life through a negative lens, to know what we want only by knowing what we don't want.

In that moment when my osteopath suggested that the problem

might lie in my unconscious, the thought that kept bothering me was, 'If that is true, then this is the ultimate in self-sabotage.' And it is. It's profoundly difficult to accept. It certainly was for me. Remember, our unconscious minds accept everything we think as fact. When we think 'What if I can't get pregnant?', the unconscious just feeds that thought with more evidence for that feeling, more experiences of *can't*.

According to the Law of Attraction, lack mindsets ensure that everything in our experience reinforces our lack, no matter how much we may want for the opposite to be true. If the thoughts you think, the feelings you feel and the words you speak are negatively charged, you will only receive more negativity – like attracts like.

The most important aspect of developing our self-awareness and understanding of ourselves is that **our minds do not *process* our negative statements or thoughts, our minds take everything we say and think as *fact*.**

Do you recognise any of these statements in your own thoughts and conversations?

'Nothing's working.'

'I feel like time is running out.'

'I feel like a failure.'

'My body doesn't work properly; it's failing me.'

'I feel broken.'

'What if I can't have a baby?'

'I'm worried that my partner will leave me.' [for which read, 'I'm not good enough.']

'I just know it hasn't happened/worked/isn't going to happen/work.'

Take note of your thoughts.

In this way, you will become increasingly aware of what you are attracting more of.

- What other statements do you find yourself saying/ thinking about yourself and your fertility?
- What is the feeling underlying your behaviour that you are motivated to avoid?
- What *don't* you want to happen?
- How do your answers make you feel?

Can you see how having these statements or thoughts might bring about the situations you're experiencing? These thoughts go around in your mind over fifty thousand times each and every day.

Think about how many days you have been on your fertility journey for and multiply it by fifty thousand. Six years equals more than two thousand days, which equates to **over one hundred million negative and repetitive thoughts**.

One negative thought isn't going to have much effect, perhaps even one whole day of negative thoughts might not either. What we need to be alert to is our sustained negative thought patterns, many of which have been part of who we have become over a period of many years.

It's time for a change.

Fertility mindset principle 5) Accepting abundance

To be whole, and to feel whole, is what we are all searching for. We tend to seek wholeness from outside of ourselves, often in our relationships. We tend to subscribe to the idea that someone else will complete us.

Shifting the gears of our limiting and negative core beliefs frees us from the belief that we have no control over our thoughts, our feelings or our lives. It helps us to realise that we are whole just as we are, that nothing and no one can complete us.

It may seem nothing short of miraculous to go from a place of despair about your fertility struggles to living an abundant (while still technically considered 'infertile') life. I came to the realisation myself that **it is a fallacy to believe that misery and 'infertility' are mutually exclusive**. I couldn't see how practising gratitude and accepting abundance could change what I was going through. It may not be possible or within your control to change or 'fix' your fertility; what can change is your perception of your fertility, how you feel and come to terms with it.

When I attempted to control and bend my fertility to my will, I was met with turmoil and deep anguish. Realising I had control of how I responded to my fertility was freeing. It means *I* get to choose. I get to choose what I focus on, what I want my life to look like and what I want from it. I know the concept of abundance might feel abstract. Personal abundance refers to a feeling of abounding fullness, of joy and strength in mind, body, spirit, and soul. I know it feels intangible, hard to grasp.

For me, abundance means living in the fullness of life in all areas: finances, love, fulfilment, purpose, and environment. Like 'wealth', which encompasses more than just money, and 'health', which encompasses more than physical wellbeing, abundance encompasses the fullness and completeness of life in all its glory.

Abundance will have a different meaning for everyone. Imagine feeling whole, feeling happy, content with life, in love with what you do and how you do it, rich in engaging relationships, deeply rooted in the present, profoundly connected to what's important to you, no matter what happens or doesn't happen.

In the depths of my struggles, I learned to see abundance everywhere, *especially* when I saw a pregnant woman. There was so much pain in seeing someone else achieve the very thing I desired more than anything. I wasn't sure if I could see abundance in this way. I told myself to at least try. As in any work we do to address our inner worlds and the thoughts and behaviours which do not serve us, there are no negative side effects. No one even needed to know that I was trying. I had nothing to lose.

I gave it a go. And I kept giving it a go. Eventually, I began to feel a new feeling. I began to feel **hope**. The more I saw pregnant women, the more I saw that there was an abundance of pregnant women, an **abundance of possibility** in every breath and every moment. There was abundant possibility for me to become pregnant too.

The envy, jealousy guilt and shame I felt before I began to

accept the abundance around me shut me off from seeing it, from experiencing gratitude, from any prospect of possibility.

I went from thinking 'Why me?' [Woe is me] to 'Why *not* me?'

I widened the limitations of my thoughts to embrace an understanding that I can have more children too, if I believe it, if I want it. I released the *how*.

I'm not saying this gives us control over our conception. I'm saying that if I cannot even contemplate the possibility of being able to conceive, when my '(in)fertility' is 'unexplained', has no cause, then my lack mindset will attract more of this reality.

'Whether you think you can, or you think you can't – you're right.' Henry Ford, 1947

This might not come easily. To get there we just make small shifts in our thinking and turn each thought on its head. **We flip one thought, one shift at a time.**

Accepting abundance is a practice like any other, which we can achieve with practise of the following.

Developing awareness of our thoughts helps us to identify when we are stuck in lack, or whether we are cultivating abundance. We can only know when we become more consciously aware and commit to making the choice to change.

Practising gratitude opens doors to accepting abundance. 'If you look at what you have in life, you will always have more. If you look at what you don't have in life, you will never have enough.' (Winfrey O). Each day, write ten things, however small, you are grateful for in your journal – like taking a bath, enjoying some chocolate, being alive...

Expanding awareness reduces our tendency to focus so intently on one thing such that we miss other possibilities. Loosening up your rigid thinking mind, practising meditation and noticing what's beyond your current field of perception – like the noises you hear from outside your window, the smell of a coffee brewing downstairs – encourages you to use *more* of your mind.

Focus on what's going right rewires our minds. It arrests the tendency we have to look for and prepare for the worst, for the threat that we have in our evolutionary heredity. Stepping back to achieve a more holistic view of what's happening to us enables us to see the good in our lives and to place our attention here.

Establishing affirmations by writing/journaling what we think and feel reveals to us our inner voices of fear and scarcity. We often write about what we fear most, the worst that we expect. Write out the opposite of these as they arise. Write about what you deeply desire. Use this as a source to create daily affirmations which you can refer to and repeat every day.

Nurture your passions by leaning into what you love to do or what you're good at. This builds confidence and self-belief. They will expand as where focus goes, energy flows (Robbins T). If you don't feel sure about what you're good at, get curious about what makes you happy; try new, or revisit past, hobbies or interests. We are all good at so many things when we give ourselves room to flourish.

Accepting abundance can seem an abstract concept when we first practise it. When we achieve it, it brings us only beauty and truth.

Accepting abundance means giving focus and energy to what want you love and want to expand. This focus and this energy go forth and multiply, leading you to receive more of what you love and want to expand.

Practice

Complete your own mindset shifts, flipping the negatives to positives, one thought at a time.

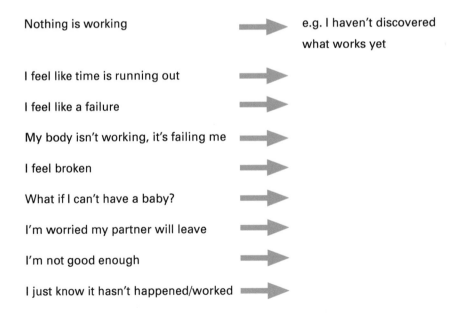

Nothing is working → e.g. I haven't discovered what works yet

I feel like time is running out →

I feel like a failure →

My body isn't working, it's failing me →

I feel broken →

What if I can't have a baby? →

I'm worried my partner will leave →

I'm not good enough →

I just know it hasn't happened/worked →

Fertility Mindset Principle
6) Finding focus

What you focus on expands. When we focus on the negative aspects of our lives, or when we are consumed by our struggles, we find more things to complain about, more frustration, more times when we notice that everybody is pregnant but us.

Just as we need to shift our mindset, shift our thoughts, we need to shift our focus. We need to refocus.

When we are so close to something, it's difficult to get perspective on it, and be able to see the whole picture, as we all know. It's the same when we are going through something – we are so '*in*' our fertility struggles, all we tend to be able to see is struggle, how hard it is, how bad we feel, how it feels like it is never going to happen.

In the grand scheme of the whole picture of your life, I'm willing to bet that not *everything* is struggle, not *everything* is hard, that good things *do* happen (and have happened) to you, that sometimes you have moments where you feel *good*. Sometimes refocusing starts with finding the one thing that is good in your life and paying attention to that. In time, you start to notice other things that are positive or good. Or even what you can do to make aspects of your life feel better.

It is indisputably hard to see light at the end of the tunnel. It's also indisputable that if you focus on the light, the light becomes stronger and clearer in your field of vision. It takes time to train your mind to keep your focus on it, no matter what challenges may come, whether progress is taking longer to come than you hoped it would. We get to choose. It's not possible to focus on positive and negative simultaneously, so we have a choice. Our brains are always more likely to present us with negative memories or thoughts when this has become habitual. This can change. You will have had positive experiences which compare with your fertility journey, or challenges that you have experienced success in along the way; you can choose to focus on these and to draw strength from them.

You can focus on mental images of what you want. Visualisation is a powerful tool that can help us to focus on what we really want. When we have images clear in our minds which produce feel-good responses, these are the images to train our minds to focus on.

Focusing isn't easy. We are used to being distracted, to having one hundred and one things to do and not enough time to do them in. Attention is perhaps the hottest commodity in the world right now. Whatever succeeds in commanding our attention wins: it generally succeeds with the use of distraction, by grabbing our attention. We are so accustomed to flitting from one distraction to the next.

Focusing on what we choose to focus on in a world that is competing for our attention first requires us to understand how our distractions succeed in catching our attention. They show us what 'everyone else' is doing, how they're living, they show us what we don't have or aren't doing. We tend to be fascinated by the people who have what we want, the women who are getting pregnant and showing us that it's possible. We are attracted to the people who are like us, those who are in the same boat and wishing they weren't. We definitely concentrate on the people who claim to have the answers, those who claim to know the diets, supplements, exercises, and/or treatments that will work for us.

Focusing requires us to turn the volume *down* on all of that noise. It makes our lives very noisy, really noisy.

Unfollow. Mute. Delete. Switch off.

When your life becomes quieter, you can tune in and focus on who you are, what you want and where you want to go. You can focus on your journey to having a baby because it is *your* journey. The journey you take to having a baby (or not) is a solo expedition, it's in the *how* you want to do it and *why* you're doing it; it's all about *you*.

When all is quiet, you can notice thoughts which stray toward the negative, to the difficulties and challenges. You get to change your mind in this way.

Focusing our minds is like training wild horses. It takes bravery, boldness, sheer determination, and persistence. It's in the falling off, having bad days, getting back up and still not giving in. We focus on what's important to us by dusting ourselves off and getting back on again. Constantly adjusting and readjusting.

Focusing, refocusing, refocusing, refocusing.

Finding focus takes repeating the practices every day, even when you don't feel like repeating them, or catching yourself thinking that they're not working.

Every day, focusing and refocusing.

JOURNAL EXERCISE

- When you step back and look at the whole picture of your life, does *everything* look bad?
- Is it really ALL bad?
- Are you able to identify at least one aspect of your life right now which *IS* good?

Finding focus: Creativity

Finding your focus will bring out creativity you never knew you had. 'Creativity' is often mistaken for 'art'. The word 'art' tends to bring out all of our judgements and negative self-criticisms; the good, the bad and the ugly. Art and creativity are often seen as being purely for people in the know, for a certain type of person. They are not.

However, this isn't about painting the Sistine Chapel. This is about creating your best life and your happiest future, your very own masterpiece. It requires you to become truly clear about how you want the picture of your life to look and feel.

When we have no clear picture of our lives, when we are inside of purely *trying* to make things happen, when we feel frustrated and uncertain, when we resort to repeating patterns and old habits to fix new challenges, **we are stuck**. The more imperfect we feel, the more we aim for perfection in ourselves and look for perfection in others, the more we are undoubtedly led to disappointment. When we are inside of perfection, trying to get things right, there is no risk, no failure, no fantasy, no painting outside the lines, no rubbing out and trying again, no working and reworking; there is no scope for change.

When we create, we work out, we invent. Creativity brings about the very solutions and resolution that we all aspire to find.

By using our creativity, we will find the solutions we need to support our future wellbeing.

Creativity requires us to be playful and without playfulness there is no change.

In 1971, DW Winnicott, paediatrician and psychoanalyst, wrote extensively about the importance of creativity and play. Winnicott defined 'play' as 'discovering the self through creative experience', and 'as a facilitation of mental growth and therefore health'. He also said that 'play' is a way of reaching the authentic, creative, less defended part of a person's personality and also that play is essential for human beings throughout their lives. Play is used in all forms of communication by adults and children. It is only through play that a child or adult is able to be creative and to reveal the full extent of her/his whole personality.

As adults, we tend not to like to think that we can play. We think that somehow we lose the ability. Similarly, many of us believe that creativity is somehow reserved for trendy young people who work for trend-setting organisations. However, Winnicott reminds us that there are many ways in which adults play – through art-making most obviously, but also when they engage in sports, hobbies, in humour, light-hearted conversation and so on. At any age, when people (children or adults) play, they feel real, they feel spontaneous, alive, and keenly interested in what they are doing. Winnicott suggested that it is *by being creative* we remain alive, and that we are alive *because we are creative*.

In fact, we humans are creative by nature. For me, the images we are able to create in our minds are a fascinating aspect of our ability to create. Our imaginations can take us into multiple futures and are capable of creating inventions and new ideas. Our imaginations have infinite potential. You may think that you don't have it in you to be creative.

Close your eyes and think about your kitchen in all its details. Think about the taps, the cupboards, the oven, the fridge, and just like that, you are able to re-create it in your own mind, like you are standing right in it. I'm willing to bet that you are able to create your kitchen in your mind's eye, and perhaps even your dream kitchen too. The possibilities are endless when we are creative.

It doesn't matter how, or if, you know how to make them happen, what matters is recognising that our minds are the seat of our creativity and creation.

The images you create in your mind create your reality. Don't like your reality? You can change the images in your mind. When we imagine new images of what we want, of how we want our lives to be, we are able to focus on them and hold them in our minds until they become our reality.

We all tend to worry about wanting things and trying to make them happen. We worry that if we imagine the future and it doesn't happen for us, we will be disappointed. In fact, we are manifesting all the time. We manifest for ourselves the good, the bad and the ugly. We manifest what we think about, what we create in our minds, whether we like them or not.

In essence, infertility is about a lack of creation, the lack of progeny, the lack of the miracle of creation itself in our lives. Perhaps if we change our perspectives, we will begin to see how we can develop greater and more meaningful levels of creation and creativity in our lives, how we can create the lives we want and consider how we can become more creative in battling our fertility issues as well as any other challenges we may face.

We can access that creative energy within us by reconnecting to the sacral[10] centre/chakra which is located below our navels in our womb area, and by feeling the flow of energy, of life, within us. When we control and try to avoid, we block the flow of our life. When we reconnect to the life force we all have within us, we regain a healthy state of flow. Like the tide, when we try to go against our life energy, try to swim upstream, we use it all up in fight and struggle, which leads us only to stress and unhappiness. However, when we unblock our focus and return our attention to the flow of life, things become easier, happier, and more aligned with our sense of purpose.

Equating creativity as the answer to infertility may seem naive. This is by no means my intention. The answer doesn't lie in whipping out your paintbrush. When we focus on our creativity, our fundamental ability to create, we connect with our inner selves, where creation is possible, where there are infinite possibilities and there is limitless potential. The answer lies in creating the images in our minds that we want to see in our reality, in creating the life that we want instead of living a life that we don't. Living lives which don't align with our values results in us creating lives that we want to escape from, or at the very least need to take breaks from.

Where is the harm in getting a little creative?

10   'Sacral Centre' Chakra - The sacral chakra is the second chakra. It is associated with the emotional body, sensuality, and creativity. Opening your sacral chakra allows you to 'feel' the world around and in us. As such, it's an important chakra at the foundation of our feeling of well-being. (chakras.info)

JOURNAL EXERCISE

- What images are you creating in your mind (good, bad or indifferent)?
- What would you like to change about them?
- In your wildest imagination, how would you dream of living?
- What one thing could you do today to make some of your dream images a reality?

Finding focus: Rituals

We all have habits – some good, some not so. We even have routines that we perform daily. We complete repeated actions which are necessary, often without much conscious thought or consideration, every day. Rituals can help you to find greater focus and discover more of your creativity. They can also help you to feel more confident, more positive about your fertility and/ or treatment and more able to take control of your life. Rituals don't have to be religious or spiritual.

Rituals are practices which are meaningful and have a sense of purpose.

I've used (and continue to use) rituals to build my confidence, to practise skills, to motivate me, to stir my creative energy, to reflect, to solve problems and to keep focus. There are many ways we can create rituals. They can be centred around our five senses. Depending on which sense you tend to favour, you can create a ritual which is very meaningful to you personally, a practice which will fill you with strength and confidence when you feel weak and unsure.

If you're auditory (you like to listen to music and/or the spoken word), you can speak your affirmations aloud. If you're more visual, conjuring mental images, or creating vision boards might appeal to you. If you're more kinaesthetic in your learning style, you might want to carry and/or feel an object which has meaning to you, like a gratitude or courage stone, which will become your literal touchstone for filling yourself up with courage. Perhaps you favour your sense of taste (you're 'gustatory'). If this is the case, the taste of a particular food or beverage may bring you positive feelings of being loved, or arouse soothing, happy memories. If your olfactory sense (sense of smell) is your leading sense, a certain scent or fragrance may elicit feelings of confidence in you. In general, colour is powerful. In your mind's eye, you could bathe yourself in a certain colour as you walk through your doctor's door, so that no matter what happens on the other side, you will feel equipped to cope with whatever the consultation brings.

Try focusing on gratitude, on only allowing yourself positive thoughts whenever you touch a tactile pebble in your pocket, catch a waft of an essential oil, play a particular song. Try wearing a flexible bracelet that you can snap to cue a switch in your energy, to prompt a focus on the traits you need at that time, to remind yourself to stand taller, or to speak with confidence.

My ritual, when I most want to appear confident, or I know I have a lot to say at an appointment and I want to say it with ease and grace, is to rehearse my words. I imagine, in great detail, sitting before the person in their office and I imagine the comments they may make in response, or any questions they may ask. I play out in my mind what I want to say and how I want to say it in great detail. Then I repeat it several times so that when my appointment time arrives, I feel confident, grounded and calm. Most importantly, I walk out of it knowing I've said all of what I wanted to communicate.

Flipping the Script on Infertility

Imagining whole conversations before they happen has been the most enormously helpful thing for me. I now do it when speaking at workshops and giving presentations. I've even started to do it with day-to-day matters – it helps determine how I want things to go in my day, how I want to feel. It's as if I send good vibes out ahead of me into my day, ensuring that things go the way I want them to.

I've found so much benefit in believing that I will get that parking space I need, that my journey will be smooth and safe, that I will have a good meeting, that I will get the work I need to get done completed today, that I will have a productive day. This manner of finding focus helps me to think about what it is I want from the day, rather than all the things I don't want. This is taking creativity to another level. When you hear people say, 'You can create your life!', you *can*. When I start to panic or feel stressed now, I am able to calm my thoughts by repeating to myself the outcome that I want for myself. So often, my positive outcome does happen, and I get what I was wishing for. We get what we ask for, whether we ask for it at a conscious or an unconscious level.

Create a ritual by trying different things and enjoying doing so. Think about the character traits that would serve you right now. When we want to move to the next level, we can't always get there with our current traits, we have to learn to embody those that we'll need to make us successful. Trying confidence (and other such attributes) on for size takes putting into practice and stepping into who we need and want to be. Like getting dressed every morning, we put on our confidence/resilience/positivity jackets, and we keep putting them on until they begin to feel as comfortable on us as a second skin. When you need a new skill to help you fulfil more of your dreams, you try on a new jacket and the process starts again.

All of the traits, skills, and attributes that you may think will come only with motherhood, you can begin to embrace and embody right now. Finding your focus, exploring rituals you enjoy and playing with new practices will enable you to focus on what you want. There are no rules, no right or wrong. Whatever works for you is right for you. Give yourself permission to experiment, have fun, and be playful.

JOURNAL EXERCISE
- What rituals could you begin to create?
- Which traits would help you pursue your dreams?
- What does embodying them look/sound/feel like?
- How can you make your practices feel easy and playful?
- How can you let go of needing to get things right, having a specific purpose, knowing how to do things?
- Consider how you can put down your load and take life less seriously more often.

Practice

How often do you sit down and ask yourself what your values and aspirations are?

Make it a practice to diarise a calendar appointment with yourself for thirty minutes each month (for example, on the last Friday of every month).

Take a page in your journal and mind-map or brainstorm all that comes to mind when you think about your aspirations in life and the values that you hold dear.

Fertility mindset principle 7) Creating your world with your words

Words have power.

Words have energy.

We've all heard that words can't hurt us. We've become accustomed to ignoring words which hurt us or make us feel uncomfortable. Yet we also hear that 'If you don't have a kind word to say, then don't say anything at all.' So, which is it? Do words hurt or don't they? Anyone who has been bullied, put down, criticised, or trolled knows that words certainly do have power. Words have power to hurt us, and our words have the power to hurt others.

Words spoken to, or about us, have power, especially when they come from an authority figure, a parent or a teacher. From childhood, we are told many things about ourselves: what to do, how to behave, what we can and can't do. We may have learned that the words and advice from authority figures are always right, beyond reproach. Their words are to be accepted, followed, swallowed whole, without question. In this way, we give the power over our lives – and the ways in which they can be lived – away to authorities.

Flipping the Script on Infertility

People are people, not authorities.

A woman/man puts on a white coat and she/he becomes a doctor, an authority figure for most of us. It can be hard to question a doctor because they've committed years of training to qualify as an expert in their field. Naturally, their knowledge is greater than ours.

Yet... we are the experts of *ourselves*.

I was the expert of me, yet I still found I became intimidated by 'White Coats'[11] and would easily lose my voice, so keen was I to trust in the professionals and have faith that their knowledge would 'fix' my problems.

I know this sense of disempowerment is common to women who experience 'infertility'. We go along with various, sometimes illogical, courses of treatment with hundreds of questions swirling around in our minds. If my 'infertility' is unexplained and nothing was found to be 'wrong' with my hormone levels, why was it that I had to use the contraceptive pill to manage my awful periods? When it was unexplained and my ovulation was not the problem, why was I taking Clomid? Why could no doctor explain why I couldn't get pregnant? If there was no reason why I couldn't become pregnant, why is it called unexplained secondary *infertility*?

Why *infertility*?

This word has power. You never hear women say, 'I *have* infertility,' they say, 'I'm infertile.' When we say or even think 'I'm infertile,' it's as if we admit to being sterile, unfruitful, barren, unproductive. What could possibly grow in such a landscape? It's normal, when

---

11   'White Coats' = doctors

we feel unproductive, to feel that we're not good enough.

How harmful the word 'infertility' is to your self-image, your mental health, your mindset. As a minimum, you become identified with the label, the illness, the *dis*ease and this risks perpetuating your symptoms.

The use of words can have an effect on our lives and our health, for good or ill.

While having difficulty with falling pregnant and/or carrying a baby to term may be your reality, 'infertility' removes any potential, any possibility of alternative outcomes. It disposes with the miraculous nature and wonder that is also an inexplicable part of our lives.

Having offspring is not the exclusive route to being and feeling productive as a woman, as a person.

When you identify with '**infertility**,' at some level it becomes who you think you are.

The difficulty you experience in trying to have a baby is not who you are. You are separate from your struggle. You may need to overcome the challenges it brings you; it does not have to define you.

When you hear about, read about and conduct research into **infertility** (fertility) and its treatments, be cynical, question what is being said. Ask yourself, 'Is that me?' 'Is that how I want to be defined?' 'Does this have to apply to me?' 'Is that my story?'

Ask yourself instead, 'Who and what do I want to be?'

In doing so, you can open yourself up to the possible. To miracles which sometimes happen to some people.

JOURNAL EXERCISE

- How do you talk about your fertility?
- Consider the *way* you talk about it, the story that you tell, the nature of the narrative you use when you talk to others about your experience?
- Are you able to practise meaning what you say, and saying what you mean?

Creating your world with your words: Saying what we mean and meaning what we say

The words we speak, like the thoughts we think, determine the life we live.

According to Einstein (1907), energy is neither created nor destroyed, therefore it is ever-present. Thoughts are energy which, for humans, often become words. We receive more of what we give our energy to – if we give love, we receive love; if we give hate, we receive hate; if we give gossip, we receive gossip, if we are critical, we receive criticism.

The words we use have the potential to create beauty or horror, heaven or hell. It's vital that we say what we mean to say and pay attention to how we say it.

Notice how you tell your story to a friend. Are you complaining, bemoaning your day or your lot in life, or anticipating good things to come? Experiment with talking about what is possible in your day-to-day exchanges.

Along with the seven life-changing words the osteopath shared with me, was a suggestion that I remove the words, 'trying,' 'sorry,' and 'but' from my vocabulary. What I was confident would be an easy task was, in fact, anything *but*!

'Trying'... It's common in fertility-speak to refer to 'trying to conceive' (or 'TTC' if you are familiar with how it is referred to in the trade). Do you *try* to lift your arm? No, you either lift it, or you don't. Trying doesn't imply anything productive. What tends to come to mind is a whole lot of work for little gain. It took a while to adjust to the shift in my vocabulary. Over time, I went from *'trying'* to conceive, to *'waiting'* to conceive. 'Waiting' at least carries the implication that something is coming.

In truth, we don't *try* to do anything, we're either doing or not doing. *Trying* might mean you're having sex, you're following an optimal diet for pregnancy, you're exercising, and all manner of *trying*. Yet conception itself is something that either happens or doesn't happen.

Sorry... It used to be that I said 'Sorry' very, very frequently. Do you find you do this too? Apologising has become such a default of human communication that we now use 'Sorry' in very broad terms, even when we don't truly mean it specifically, sometimes even when someone bumps into *us*. Even when we run late. Are you? Were you deliberately late? Could you help that you were? We all tend to pay conversational lip service to the word 'sorry'. In fact, what we really mean to say is that we appreciate being waited for, that we are thankful for being allowed time and patience.

'But'... is also a word which tends to be overused, not least in the dreaded context of 'Yes... *but*...' Every word which comes before 'but' in a sentence is generally worthless, meaningless, disposable. Try it. Most phrases can be greatly improved by starting our sentences after the word 'but.'

Binning the 'but' forces you to think about what you're saying (mean what you say) and it makes you more precise with your

words (say what you mean).

Practising these seemingly simple changes encourages us to think about the words we use and why, to pause rather than react, to reflect on our feelings and experiences.

Language also has different connotations for different people. Whatever language you choose to use, be aware of the outcome they may have, and the effect they may have on others. Awareness of the words you use, rather than aiming for perfection in this, will have an enormous positive effect on your life and on the lives of those around you.

You can use words with positive intentions, with expectancy of what you want to happen and to come into your life.

Open up your world to all possibilities, with the power of your words.

JOURNAL EXERCISE

- Which are the words you find you use the most?
- How might these words affect your reality?
- Are there changes to the words you use that you would benefit from changing?

TIP – Sometimes allowing yourself to pause before responding in a conversation gives you enough time to be mindful of your turn of phrase, and to substitute your habitual terms for words which convey precisely what you mean.

Practice

Aim to raise your awareness of your use of the words, 'try,' 'sorry,' and 'but.' Practise avoiding them in your conversations [whilst remembering to be kind to yourself: breaking habits takes time and patience]. Fill in your substitute words:

Instead of **'try'**   say...
Instead of **'sorry'**   say...
Instead of **'but'**   say...

Fertility Principle 8) Repetition is the mother of learning

Change requires us to regain, refocus, relearn.

In relearning, we repeat the lessons we need to help us overcome our challenges.

Repetition is key to forming new habits, as we transition our historical knowledge or learning from the conscious to the unconscious. We overwrite our old programming and conditioning with the updated and improved versions that we want to live by.

How many times do we read a self-help book through once, think how great it was, and then find that nothing has changed?

It's repetition which is the key to making successful changes in our lives. It's how children learn, without even realising. We take our default aptitude for learning for granted. As we grow, we absorb learning in formal education or in our work, with little awareness of just how much knowledge we are acquiring.

I can tell you, from a personal perspective, that without repetition I wouldn't have written this book. I digest the books I read, the videos I watch, the podcasts I listen to over and over again. I come back to them, and I will go back to them again. Repetition is the key to reprogramming our mindsets and to making sustainable change.

Flipping the Script on Infertility

I am mindful of the influences I consume. I don't watch the news; on social media, I follow those who lift and inspire; I limit the amount of violence on television or film that I watch; I tend not to read fiction, preferring to read books which will enhance my learning and my understanding of my world. Everything I consume is geared toward helping me to improve, to a deeper understanding of myself.

Everything within my environment is my choice to control. I have a choice as to what I bring into my experience. We have the power to choose how we create our worlds and our personal realities by focusing on how and who we want to be. This takes a natural process of learning, relearning and continuing to relearn.

When you read books that chime with your values, and read them again three, four or even ten times, when you listen to inspirational podcast episodes again and again, you will start to see how things might begin to change for you. Let their words sink in, allow yourself to integrate the knowledge they hold.

The practices that you put in place to support your personal development, that will see you take control of your emotions and mindset, will perhaps be difficult at first; it is only after doing them again and again that perhaps you will see benefit. Journaling, meditating, exercise, routines, structure are all practices that can become daily practices that see you achieve success and manage any challenges that you may face.

Storms will come, new challenges will need to be faced. Flipping the script on our fertility gives us the tools and the knowledge to overcome any of life's challenges. Repeat, repeat, repeat...

JOURNAL EXERCISE

- What influences on your environment would you like to limit?
- Are you able to identify the people or media which cause you anxiety or promote negativity?
- Which books, programmes, or voices do you find interesting or inspiring? Make a commitment to reading, watching or listening to them again (and then again).
- What other positive influences or activities can you bring into your day-to-day experience?
- Who could you follow or learn more about?

Practice

Choose a single book to read or an interview/podcast to listen to. Make notes of what you discovered or learned and how it relates to your situation after the first read-through or listen. Commit to reading or listening to this again in any spare moment that you have. After each complete round, make a note of a new discovery, and then make a plan of how you are going to make this new discovery a part of your daily practice. Each time you find a new book or podcast which interests or motivates you, keep it on repeat, noting the discoveries you make after each and every repetition.

Conclusion

Flipping the Script on Infertility

We have certainly travelled far and deep. We have journeyed into the past and imagined into the future. We have discovered old fears and learned new truths. We have excavated the deepest parts of ourselves and revealed who we are in all our beautiful (ugly) truth.

My story is by no means unique and I share it here to let you know that you are not alone. The journey I have made out of infertility, through self-discovery to fulfilment and purpose, you can make (and I hope will make) too.

While I have not told you *how* to get pregnant, my intention for you is that by working through the Fertility Mindset Principles you will start and embark on a road to transformation and transition into motherhood and/or into a life of fulfilment.

I implore you to release the *how*, the how keeps us stuck, find your peace in the unknown. I encourage you to own your 'ugly (beautiful) truths', no one is all perfect, so embrace the fact that you are imperfectly perfect. I recommend you work through the Fertility Mindset Principles at your pace and return to them again and again – remember repetition is the mother of learning, the mother of creating a new habit and is the eighth (and probably most important) principle. Make the commitment to overcoming yourself every day. This work is never done. This work is a lifetime practice. And if you're up for the challenge, it can be a practice you relish. I live to overcome myself every day, to keep learning the lesson until I have learned the lesson, to discovering what works, to living a life of abundance.

The secret to this book and any practice is in the commitment to the work – making the daily practices, reading it in its entirety or carefully chosen parts again and again, let the words, the thinking, the awakened feelings sink into your subconscious, let the process of flipping your script become a part of who you are.

Use this book and use your journal like self-therapy for overcoming any life crises. Infertility is a life crisis that you will get through and if you can get through it, you can get through anything that life has to offer. You are a warrior – and don't you forget it. If you have journaled throughout, then go back and reflect on what you have written, note what has changed, what you are finding difficult, what needs work and see how far you have come.

I wrote this book for women who, like I once did, feel lost in life and incomplete, who are without direction and purpose, and through the experience of infertility, these feelings can no longer be ignored. I wrote this for you because I don't want you to struggle on your own. I wrote this for you because in all of the fertility information out there, nobody is talking to you about what really matters – you.

Whether or not our individual dreams of motherhood are realised, we matter. You matter.

I want to leave you with this last thought:

How long do you plan to live?

Strange question? Perhaps… however, it's one that I have asked myself and the women that I work with. Infertility is time standing still and rushing ahead all in the same breath. Counting cycles, getting older, looking ahead to when and when and when. Infertility is living the same month over and over for many years. It's completely normal because the fear that has been created around time as a limited resource in our society is unbearable. We all get the same time, it's what you do with it that matters.

That question is the final challenge to get you to reframe your thinking, to reframe the fear and anxiety. When we look at our lives right now it seems like there isn't enough time. When you think about how long you want to live, you will see there is plenty of time, in fact depending on how long that is, it might seem like too much time.

There is a need to change our relationship with time. I'm not talking about age. I'm talking about time and reframing the fear that time is running out.

This is mindset shifting. This is shifting from no time to plenty of time. This is shifting out of fear into calm confidence.

You have the tools now. You know what mindset shifting is. You know the power that there is in making practices to take back control of your life.

You have plenty of time.
Live a full life. Live abundant.
It matters to your future family. You matter to your future family.
You matter.

Epilogue

Flipping the Script on Infertility

My story is by no means over. In fact, it has only just begun. I opened this book with a quote that I feel encompasses my life, our lives and the many obstacles we all face. Everyone's journey has its purpose.

When I was in the eye of my challenged-by-fertility storm, there was no way I could have seen my purpose. I couldn't possibly have known that it would lead me to write these words. I did have a deep knowing that there would be reasons for me going through what I was going through. I believe it wholeheartedly when I say that I believe *everything* happens for a reason.

There is a reason you are reading this book now. There is a reason for everything that is happening in your life. The fertility journeys that at some level we share brought me here and to share with you what I learned from mine. When I stood at the beginning of my fertility trials, I was stalked by the word 'hope' and plagued by the word 'despair'. Hope seemed just too, too far beyond my grasp, not grounded in any version of my reality. Hope was always fleeting – it lasted about two weeks, the two weeks leading to ovulation – and just as quickly, fell away into a certain knowing that hope had given way to disappointment, again.

I called it hopeless hope, a wishful thinking kind of hope that I allowed myself, which wasn't actually anchored in any positivity or in any firm belief. Hope was the kind of wish that children make when they blow out their candles on a cake, the ones that never come true. When our hopes are dashed repeatedly, we end up surrendering to what we expected all along – failure.

Hope coupled with expected failure can only bring about failure.

Flipping the Script on Infertility

Our expectations will always outweigh our hopes. **Hope coupled with belief is powerfully different.** There can be no disputing how hard belief can be when you have lived with disappointment for so long. Many of us have a belief in things and people we can't see, touch or evidence so why not have faith in our own bodies? Why not restore our belief in becoming a mother?

I had to find my way to developing my own firm belief deep in the core of who I am. Meditation, having a clear vision (and practising visualisation) of a future that I wanted to live in, along with releasing my *how* helped above all else. Meditation paired with visualisation can be extremely powerful because the images come from within you, the highest version of you. Visualisation gives you inner confidence and images you can believe in. There was a time when I wouldn't allow myself to picture the future because it just felt too much, too wild and impossible. It was a game-changing moment when I realised that **when it comes to picturing the things we want, the *how* isn't important.**

We tend to picture the things we want and then quickly become overloaded by anxiety about the *how* it is going to happen. Then we try to force it to happen with our '*trying*', when all this does is send a huge signal that you have no faith to the universe. You try to prescribe the *how*.

Allowing life to flow through us will allow life to come to us on its own terms, whether this is a new baby, a change of direction, a renewed sense of purpose.

Release your *how*.

Flipping the Script on Infertility

Releasing the *how* has changed my life. My concern is *what* I want and need in my life. My concern is no longer the *how*.

It has taken me a long time to become clear about my wants. I urge you to get clear about yours, in as much detail as you can. Let yourself imagine.

Be playful with your wants.

We hamper our imagination with knowledge. Just as our *how* stops us knowing what we want in life, knowledge stops us from dreaming and creating, from making leaps and taking risks. The truth is, we can't always *know*.

In eight years without using contraception, I wondered how it was even possible that we had not one single pregnancy. I used to think that if someone could put me out of my misery with facts and knowledge, I would be OK. That I'd be fine if a medical professional were to just say to me, 'You know, you only get to have the one child,' or, 'Yes, you definitely will have another one day.' I thought and I believed that not only would I cope better in full possession of the 'facts'; more than that, I *needed* that fact.

Therapy training introduced me to the initially vague and intangible concept of the 'fertile void'. A touchstone of Gestalt psychotherapy, it plays a key role in the cycle of awareness that is intrinsic to this form of therapy. In the fertile void, creative energy is said to flow from experiencing the emptiness of being, from the ability to stay in a state of unknowing and to trust in the flow of life. It encapsulates the feeling of emptiness I felt and the, albeit miserable, hope that I clung to. It also encapsulates what I now know to be true. That within my (and your) emptiness, there is so much richness, so much fertile ground. All it takes to become unstuck is to change our perspective.

Trusting in the flow of life in a state of unknowing may feel incomprehensible as you navigate your way through fertility/'infertility' challenges. **It's impossible to achieve without awareness, particularly self-awareness, without an understanding of the feelings you repress, of your unconscious, your conditioning, your resentments and negativity, of the power of your reactive mind, and its sometimes unhelpful thoughts.**

It is by addressing our mindsets that we can begin to grasp a difference between understanding and knowing. We live in a time in society where it is the norm to want to *know*, to know what's coming and how to approach it, to feel ready and able to predict and react. The fertile void, in contrast, offers an invitation to accept that possibilities come from not knowing all the answers, it is from the unknown that new lives emerge.

Being in a state of unknowing is uncomfortable; for many of us, it's unbearable – it brings anguish, frustration, and resistance. There are few challenges more unbearable than the unknowing which comes with the fertility treatment process and involves a necessary state of limbo. The one thing which would make it easier to bear, more liveable with, would be to know whether or not there would one day be a pregnancy, a child. At present, this is a kind of fortune-telling which is unavailable to all of us. We yearn for knowledge that we cannot acquire, no matter how hard we try. We look to others to give us a knowledge which none of us have. At the time of writing, my state of unknowing continues to be uninformed by exactly when I might have another child.

Developing my awareness and flipping the script on my own mindset means I am no longer plagued by the anguish, frustration, and despair of *trying*, with needing to *know*. It means I no longer strive for results I cannot control, and I no longer resist the flow of life. I have found comfort and ease in living in a state of acceptance of what is and what will be.

Beginning to see where you are on your fertility journey as a fertile void, will offer you a starting point for your self-reflection, a place to just be. It will invite you to consider infinite possibilities, limitless potential, positive and healing change.

We experience life-changing events when our route to parenthood is not straightforward for us, when we realise it lies beyond our control. In the unknowing we experience the quiet changes, the infinitesimally minute steps we take that can bring about change for us personally, and for our families, friends and communities.

We have become so accustomed to seeing the extraordinary in our lives every day that we are no longer satisfied with our own 'ordinary'. Not one of us is ordinary. We have such potential to learn and to relearn. With our fertility challenges, for every so-called solution we come across, there is one that may not make it happen for us. There is so much unknowing in not yet knowing what might work. Perhaps a truth within these pages may lead you to find the knowing that you need.

Healing takes time. We've become accustomed to getting what we want quickly in our lives. It takes time to heal at mental, emotional, spiritual, *and* physical levels.
What would a sense of harmony and balance in all four elements of your inner world look and feel like for you?

Letting go can bring harmony at every level. Letting go of what we *think* our lives *should* be, of who we *think* we are and *should* be, of our core negative beliefs, of the unhelpful thought patterns and of the pressures we put on ourselves and hinder us, is powerfully healing.

My story is your story is our story.

Our stories tell of what it means to be human, woman, daughter, sister, partner, mother-in-waiting. Mothers-in-waiting who live, and need to function, in these times.

**An 'infertility' diagnosis, or a decision to choose to undergo fertility treatment, does not define you unless you let it.
Becoming a mother will not define you.
Choosing happiness and fulfilment for yourself and for your family, in your life and in your relationships, will define you.
We have the power to be the change we want to see in our world both now and in the future that we want for ourselves and any children we may have.
The void is not infertile.**

About the Author

Kezia Ashley Okafor is a Fertility Mindset Coach and Infertility Counsellor, working with women struggling with the emotional distress of infertility. Helping them to take charge of their emotions and mindset, so they feel in control of their infertility journey and life, which maximises their chances for a successful and healthy pregnancy.

Kezia is a wife, mother, and runs her own online business. Kezia's mission is to bring support and resources to the many millions of women globally facing infertility in isolation. Kezia's own experience of infertility and experiencing the lack of emotional support has spurred her to 'plug the gap' on mental and emotional health knowledge within the fertility community.

As a qualified art therapist and counsellor and using her personal experiences, Kezia has a unique approach to therapeutic techniques that can facilitate transformation and change, as demonstrated in this book.

Stay connected with Kezia here:

 www.keziaokafor.com

 facebook.com/theinfertilitycounsellor

 instagram.com/theinfertilitycounsellor
instagram.com/kezia_ashley_okafor

 twitter.com/kezia_okafor

Acknowledgements

I have to start by thanking my biggest 'cheerleader', for supporting me and believing in me even before I believed in myself – my amazing husband Michael. We have been through so much and you remain my rock throughout. Who knows where life will take us, here's to the (continued) journey.

To my little man Elijah, thank you for making me a mother and it's because of you that I even had the courage to write this. Everything I do is for you; I live to make you proud. You make everything worth it.

The (infamous) Osteopath Anton Micallef, those seven little words changed my life, you are an amazing coach; without the mindset work I couldn't be where I am today. There surely are no coincidences in life and our meeting certainly proves that.

The best editor ever Vanessa J. Anderson, I am eternally grateful that we have created this magic together. Your passion for my words and my message has been incredible from the start, you have elevated my words and thoughts. Let's make more magic in the future!

Suzy Ashworth, you are truly an amazing human being, thank you for your wisdom and for showing me what's possible.

Training to be a therapist was one of the most amazing experiences of my life, which happened to coincide with the darkest – fertility treatment! So special thanks to the amazing ladies on the IATE Advanced Diploma, we travelled together for two life-transforming years – you brought me back to life. Thanks also to the amazing lecturers at the Institute for Art Therapy and Education (IATE), your profound insights and knowledge are the bedrock for all that I do.

My family: Mum, Dad, Ben, my powerhouse Aunties, my grandparents who made the journey to the UK, without you all I (of course) wouldn't be here. You all have supported me and my little family, you have held us in good times and bad, and for that I am beyond grateful.

Lastly, I must thank my early readers who helped to steer me in the right direction – Sadari Shakes, Antoinette Daley and Elizabeth Mpyisi; your feedback was invaluable.

Finally, to my community of followers, to the amazing women I have the privilege to work with – you all inspire me to do this work, you inspire me every day to keep going.

Thank you.

Glossary

Basal body temperature (BBT) – your temperature when you are fully at rest. Ovulation may cause a slight increase in basal body temperature. By tracking your basal body temperature each day, you may be able to predict when you ovulate.

Cervical mucus – fluid secreted by the cervix, the production of which is stimulated by the hormone oestrogen. Throughout the menstrual cycle, the amount and quality of mucus that is produced will fluctuate, and by observing these changes you can begin to predict the most fertile days in your cycle.

Chakras – are the concentrated energy centres of the body. Chakra is a Sanskrit term and it means 'wheel' or 'disk' and is derived from the root word 'cakra'. Chakras are spinning wheels of energy/light.

Cognitive distortions – habitual ways of thinking that are often inaccurate, irrational and negatively biased.

Democratic Unionist Party (DUP) – a unionist political party in Northern Ireland favouring British identity, founded in 1971.

Endometriosis – a condition where small pieces of the womb lining (the endometrium) start growing in other places, such as the ovaries.

Existential crisis – existential, it has to do with human existence. An existential crisis occurs when a person questions the meaning of their life and of existence itself.

Fibroids – non-cancerous growths that develop in or around the womb (uterus).

Intracytoplasmic sperm injection (**ICSI**) – is the most common and successful treatment for severe male infertility. In the ICSI process, a tiny needle, called a micropipette, is used to inject a single sperm into the centre of the egg.

Intrauterine insemination (**IUI**) – is one of the most straightforward forms of assisted fertility treatments, the goal of which is to increase the number of sperm that reach and fertilise the egg on their own. It involves placing sperm inside a woman's uterus to facilitate fertilisation.

In vitro fertilisation (**IVF**) – a process of fertilisation where an egg is combined with sperm outside the body, in vitro. The process involves monitoring and stimulating a woman's ovulatory process, removing an ovum or ova from the woman's ovaries and letting sperm fertilise them in a liquid in a laboratory.

Law of Attraction – the belief that positive or negative thoughts bring positive or negative experiences into a person's life.

Flipping the Script on Infertility

National Health Service (**NHS**) – the publicly funded healthcare system in the United Kingdom (UK).

'**Netflix & Chill**' – Netflix is the popular TV- and movie-streaming service. Chill is a verb that, in this context, means relaxing. Netflix and chill, as a distinct phrase, means to watch Netflix with a romantic prospect, with the eventual expectation of sexual activity.

Ovulation – is the release of an egg from one of a woman's ovaries. After the egg is released, it travels down the fallopian tube, where fertilisation by a sperm cell may occur.

Polycystic ovary syndrome (**PCOS**) – a common condition that affects how a woman's ovaries work.

Pelvic inflammatory disease (PID)– infection of the upper female genital tract, which includes the womb, fallopian tubes and ovaries.

Psyche – refers to all of the elements of the human mind, both conscious and unconscious, or referring to a person's emotional life.

Psychosomatic – (of a physical illness or other condition) caused or aggravated by a mental factor such as internal conflict or stress.

Shero – a woman admired or idealised for her courage, outstanding achievements, or noble qualities, a heroine.

Stress – can be defined as the degree to which you feel overwhelmed or unable to cope as a result of pressures that are unmanageable.

Stressor – chemical or biological agent, environmental condition, external stimulus or an event seen as causing stress to an organism. Psychologically speaking, a stressor can be events or environments that individuals might consider demanding, challenging, and/or threatening individual safety.

Timed intercourse – a simple treatment option for infertility. It involves monitoring your ovarian cycle via ultrasound and hormone testing and then having sexual intercourse around the time you are predicted to be most fertile.

TTC – Trying to conceive.

World Health Organization (WHO) – an agency of the United Nations, established in 1948 with headquarters in Geneva, responsible for coordinating international health activities, and aiding governments in improving health services.

References

Ackerman CE, **What is Self-Image and How Do We Improve it?** 2020 (https://positivepsychology.com/self-image/)

A Davis and R Hilmantel, **This Is Why We Chose To Talk About Black Women And Infertility**, 2018 (https://www. womenshealthmag.com/health/a23785945/black-women-infertility-letter-from-the-editors/)

American Public Media, **Business Is Prospering**, 2018 (http:// americanradioworks.publicradio.org/features/fertility_race/part3/ section1.shtml)

Ashley Wiltshire, Lynae M Brayboy, Kiwita Phillips, et al, **Infertility knowledge and treatment beliefs among African American women in an urban community**, Contracept Reprod Med.v.4; 2019, PMC6757383 (https://www.ncbi.nlm.nih.gov/pmc/ articles/PMC6757383/)

Burton N, **What's the Difference Between an Emotion and a Desire?** 2016 (https://www.psychologytoday.com/gb/blog/hide-and-seek/201603/whats-the-difference-between-emotion-and-desire)

CDC, Infertility Service Use in the United States: Data From the National Survey of Family Growth, 1982–2010 (https://www.cdc.gov/nchs/data/nhsr/nhsr073.pdf)

CDC, 2006-2010 National Survey of Family Growth, (https://resolve.org/infertility-101/what-is-infertility/fast-facts/)

Dewar G, **Stress hormones during pregnancy,** 2008 (https://www.parentingscience.com/Stress-hormones-during-pregnancy.html)

Duffy's Napa Valley Treatment, **How long does it take to break the habit of an addiction?** 2013 (https://www.duffysrehab.com/about/blog/how-long-does-it-take-to-break-the-habit-of-addiction/)

Eagleson H, **Your Chances of Getting Pregnant at Every Age,** (https://www.parents.com/getting-pregnant/trying-to-conceive/up-your-chances-of-getting-pregnant-at-every-age/)

Economist, **The fertility business is booming,** 2019 (https://www.economist.com/business/2019/08/08/the-fertility-business-is-booming)

Faith, Hope & Psychology, **80 % of Thoughts Are Negative...95 % are repetitive,** 2012, (https://faithhopeandpsychology.wordpress.com/2012/03/02/80-of-thoughts-are-negative-95-are-repetitive/)

Fertility Network UK, **Let down: lack of support for fertility patients before, during and after treatment,** 2017 (https://fertilitynetworkuk.org/wp-content/uploads/2016/06/Press-Release-Let-down-lack-of-fertility-counselling-support-April-2017.pdf)

Formica MJ, **5 Steps for Being Present**, 2011 (https://www.psychologytoday.com/gb/blog/enlightened-living/201106/5-steps-being-present)

Frankl V, **Man's Search for Meaning**, (1959) Beacon Press

Gaba S, **The Mother Wound**, 2019 (https://www.psychologytoday.com/gb/blog/addiction-and-recovery/201910/the-mother-wound)

Grand View Research, **IVF Market Size Worth $37.7 Billion By 2027** (https://www.grandviewresearch.com/press-release/global-ivf-market)

Gurevich R, **The Chances for IVF Pregnancy Success**, 2020 (https://www.verywellfamily.com/what-are-the-chances-for-ivf-success-1960213#citation-1)

Harvard Health Publishing, **The psychological impact of infertility and its treatment**, 2009 (https://www.health.harvard.edu/newsletter_article/The-psychological-impact-of-infertility-and-its-treatment)

Hoff HS, Crawford NM, Mersereau JE, **Screening for Psychological Conditions in Infertile Women: Provider Perspectives**, 2017 (https://pubmed.ncbi.nlm.nih.gov/29185847/)

Jeffrey S, **Repressed Emotions: A Guide to Understanding Feelings Hidden Within Us (And How to Transmute Them)**, (https://scottjeffrey.com/repressed-emotions/)

Kowitt B, **The Fertility Industry: Inside the big business of babymaking,** 2020 (https://fortune.com/longform/fertility-business-femtech-investing-ivf/)

Lindsay J, **What are the success rates for IVF and how much does it cost?** 2018 (https://metro.co.uk/2018/11/08/what-are-the-success-rates-for-ivf-and-how-much-does-it-cost-2-8110625/?ito=cbshare)

MBRRACE-UK - Saving Lives, Improving Mothers' Care 2019. Knight M, Bunch K, Tuffnell D, Shakespeare J, Kotnis R, Kenyon S, Kurinczuk JJ (Eds.) on behalf of MBRRACE-UK. Saving Lives, Improving Mothers' Care - Lessons learned to inform maternity care from the UK and Ireland Confidential Enquiries into Maternal Deaths and Morbidity 2015-17. Oxford: National Perinatal Epidemiology Unit, University of Oxford 2019. (https://www.npeu.ox.ac.uk/assets/downloads/mbrrace-uk/reports/MBRRACE-UK%20Maternal%20Report%202019%20-%20WEB%20VERSION.pdf)

Maggie O'Farrell, **Why many women are unable to have a second child,** 2010, (https://www.theguardian.com/lifeandstyle/2010/may/07/secondary-infertility-increasing)

Meyer C, **EMOTIONS VERSUS FEELINGS,** 2012 (https://emotionaldetective.typepad.com/emotional-detective/2012/04/emotions-vs-feelings.html)

MGH Center for Women's Mental Health, **Fertility and Mental Health,** 2018 (https://womensmentalhealth.org/specialty-clinics/infertility-and-mental-health/)

Murphy J, **The Power of your Subconscious Mind**, 1963

NHS, **Causes of infertility** (https://www.nhs.uk/conditions/
infertility/causes/)

NHS, **IVF** (https://www.nhs.uk/conditions/ivf/)

Ozbay F, et al, **Social Support and Resilience to Stress**, 2007,
Psychiatry (Edgmont)v.4(5); PMC2921311, (https://www.ncbi.nlm.
nih.gov/pmc/articles/PMC2921311/)

Prasanta Kumar Deka, Swarnali Sarma, **Psychological aspects
of infertility**, 2010, BJMP 2010;3(3):a336 (https://www.bjmp.org/
content/psychological-aspects-infertility)

Rooney KL, Domar AD, **The relationship between Stress and
Infertility**, 2018 (https://www.ncbi.nlm.nih.gov/pmc/articles/
PMC6016043/)

Stewart LM, Holman CD, Hart R, Finn J, Mai Q, Preen DB.
**How effective is in vitro fertilization, and how can it be
improved?** Fertil Steril. 2011 Apr;95(5):1677-83. doi:10.1016/j.
fertnstert.2011.01.130.

Townsend R, **The Lasting Trauma of Infertility**, 2019 (https://
www.nytimes.com/2019/10/23/parenting/the-lasting-trauma-of-
infertility.html)

Warren-Gash Dr, **Worldwide infertility rates unchanged in 20 years says World Health Organisation**, 2013, (https://www.bionews.org.uk/page_93930)

WHO, **Mental health: strengthening our response**, 2018, (https://www.who.int/news-room/fact-sheets/detail/mental-health-strengthening-our-response)

WHO, **Infertility is a global public health issue**, (https://www.who.int/reproductivehealth/topics/infertility/perspective/en/)

Winnicott DW, **Playing and Reality**, (1971) Routledge Classics

Wong C, **How Emotions and Organs Are Connected in Traditional Chinese Medicine**, 2020 (https://www.verywellmind.com/emotions-in-traditional-chinese-medicine-88196)

Yontef G, **Gestalt Therapy: An Introduction**, 1993 (https://www.gestalt.org/yontef.htm)